D1158178

OUR TREES
HOW TO KNOW THEM

A NORTHERN LANDSCAPE SHOWING THE PICTURESQUE EFFECT OF THE CONIFERS—PINES, SPRUCES AND FIRS

OUR TREES
HOW TO KNOW THEM

PHOTOGRAPHS FROM NATURE

By

ARTHUR I. EMERSON

WITH A GUIDE TO THEIR RECOGNITION AT ANY
SEASON OF THE YEAR AND NOTES ON THEIR
CHARACTERISTICS, DISTRIBUTION, AND CULTURE

By

CLARENCE M. WEED, D.Sc.

TEACHER OF NATURE STUDY IN THE MASSACHUSETTS STATE NORMAL SCHOOL AT LOWELL

FIFTH EDITION
WITH AN ILLUSTRATED INTRODUCTION

GARDEN CITY BOOKS
GARDEN CITY, NEW YORK

PREFACE

THE following pages are intended to furnish an opportunity for a more intimate acquaintance with our American trees. The pictures upon the plates have in all cases been taken direct from nature, and have been brought together in such a way that the non-botanical reader can recognize at a glance either the whole tree or the leaves, flowers, fruits or winter twigs, and thus be able to identify with ease and certainty any unknown tree to which his attention may be called. In the discussions of the text especial attention has been given to the distinguishing characteristics of the various species, as well as to the more interesting phases of the yearly cycle of each and the special values of each for ornamental planting.

In the making of the pictures the trees growing in a wild state have been utilized wherever possible, although in the case of a number of rare or local species advantage has been taken of the unrivalled collection of trees in the Arnold Arboretum, a privilege for which we are indebted to the kind permission of the Director, Professor Charles Sprague Sargent, and the helpful assistance of his associates, especially Messrs. C. E. Faxon, W. J. Dawson, and J. G. Jack. In the case of a few trees we are also under obligations for material to the authorities of the Harvard Botanic Garden, and the Boston Public Gardens. We are indebted to the Forest Service of the U. S. Department of Agriculture for the pictures of the trees of the Eucalyptus and the Long-leaved Pine and to the Arnold Arboretum for a few of the other pictures on the plates.

In the sequence of the trees in the book, as well as in the mooted question of the technical names, we have followed Professor Sargent's classic "Manual of the Trees of North America," giving also in some cases additional names used in standard books.

INTRODUCTION

WHETHER we realize it or not our interest in trees is due largely to their changes through the yearly cycle. Summer, autumn, winter, spring—how the trees differ with the seasons, often changing visibly from day to day and always making the chief element in the great panoramas of the landscape. More than anything else they give the prevailing tone to each succeeding season.

While these changes seem so sudden—a maple covered with leaves yesterday showing but bare branches to-day, a bare twig of apple to-day becoming a bower of blossoming beauty to-morrow—they are all carefully provided for long in advance. I once asked a class of high school graduates when the tree buds were formed. "In winter," was the ready reply. And this I judge would have been the answer of the average man on the street. Yet the tree began to develop those buds for next year's growth almost as soon as it began to grow this year. And it kept on with the good work all through the spring and summer, continuing even into autumn until the buds were fully formed, covered with protecting scales, and furnished in twig and trunk and root with sufficient materials for the rapid start into new growth another year. Then only did each leaf send back to the twig its last reserves of food and begin to loosen its hold, taking on beautiful autumnal colors and finally dropping to the ground to disintegrate, and even in death supplying to the tree that gave it birth, materials for further growth.

As a result of these seasonal diversities we can not know even our commonest trees until we have summered and wintered with them, studying them also in the intervening autumn and spring. So the student of trees has always a valid excuse for an excursion out-of-doors—a better one than Thoreau's pursuit of last year's birds' nests—and if he is sufficiently in earnest to make careful comparisons of the various parts he can always find material to add to his tree herbarium.

Most people willingly acknowledge the beauty and interest of the trees in the bloom of spring, the foliage of summer, or the glory of autumn, but their interest wanes in winter. Seemingly they are content to think that the trees then are only

"Bare ruined choirs
Where late the sweet birds sang."

Yet it is true that at no season can one get a better understanding of the trees than in winter. At this time the characteristic features of their growth stand out distinctly. The outlines against the sky, the bark upon the trunks, the manner of branching, the distinctive features of twigs and buds—these are best seen in the dormant season when the obscuring leaves have disappeared.

As I have already said in another book,[1] one of the most interesting ways to know a tree is to be able to recognize it at a distance by its general outline. It is surprising how easy such recognition becomes to one who looks for the distinguishing characters of tree growth. Many trees may be known almost as far as they can be seen, and it is a real pleasure to name them when one goes swiftly by in

THE INTERMINGLING BRANCHES OF THE SWAMP WHITE-OAK

trolley, train, or automobile, or to pick them out from afar when enjoying a ramble over the highway.

There are two distinctive types of tree outlines, due to the two ways in which the main trunk develops. In some trees it grows straight up, sending out branches along its sides but continuing clear to the top. Such a tree represents the *excurrent* mode of growth: the pin oak and the balsam poplar are good examples. In other trees the main trunk divides into several large branches to make an open vase-like form. These represent the *deliquescent* mode of growth: the American elm and the

[1] "Seeing Nature First." J. B. Lippincott Company, Philadelphia.

A WINTER SCENE COMBINING DECIDUOUS TREES AND EVERGREENS

white willow are familiar examples. This character of the trees is especially easy to study in winter because the trunk is readily seen through the leafless branches. Many of the pictures of dormant trees on the plates in this book illustrate this phase of tree growth. In looking at them, as in looking at the trees outdoors, you soon find that more trees are deliquescent than excurrent and you also discover that it is not always easy to tell to which type some trees belong, for Nature seldom has hard and fast dividing lines to make our classification easy.

Next to the outlines as revealed against the sky the most striking features of the winter trees are found in the bark of the trunks. The mottled blacks and whites of the birches are more familiar to many people through the pictures of the

TREES BECOME OF GREATEST INTEREST IN SPRING

artists than from the trees themselves. For numberless photographs and paintings have recorded the play of light and shade upon these trees and the results are to be seen wherever pictures hang on walls. Among our native species the canoe or paper birch stands preëminent in this respect: the shimmering light upon the white bark is reflected in a thousand directions from the ragged rolls that peel off along the surface of the trunk and larger branches. The English white and our own gray birches have this beauty to a less degree, while the trunks of the red, the yellow and the black birches each have distinctive though less striking features. Perhaps the beech, almost as great a favorite with the artists as the birch, should rank next in one's affection. The smooth, light-reflecting gray bark enables one to know a beech of any size as far as it can be seen.

Even the twigs on the leafless trees have such definite characteristics that the various species are easily recognized. The position, shape and color of the leaf buds and the flower buds, the location and markings of the leaf scars, the color and texture of the bark of different years of growth, the number and size of the lenticels or breathing pores of the bark—all these are features by which the tree may be known. Not only may we tell a maple from a poplar but we can tell which maple or which poplar a given twig belongs to.

The statement that the trees have provided the season before for the starting into spring growth is easily verified. Cut off a twig bearing leaf buds and flower buds. Put the cut end in a jar of water in a warm moist atmosphere and see how the leaves and flowers develop from the water and the food materials stored up in the branch. It is very much the same sort of provision that is made by a kernel of corn for starting the young plant on its life journey. In both cases there is provision to keep things going until the expanded leaves can begin working in the sunlight to manufacture food materials.

While the trees are reduced to their simplest elements in winter they become of greatest interest in spring—the time when they change so rapidly from day to day and week to week. These changes are chiefly due to the pushing out of leaves and flowers. In general the catkin-bearing trees—like the alders, the birches and hornbeams, the willows and the hickories—send out their flowers in advance of the leaves, while the petal-bearing blossoms of the other trees appear with the leaves or after they are well developed.

Some Little Known Trees

In addition to the many trees, native or naturalized, more or less commonly found in the eastern region of North America which are discussed in the following pages there are a number of others that deserve mention. Most of these have been recently introduced and are now offered in the larger nurseries for planting in streets, parks or home-grounds. Some are so well adapted to such uses that they are bound to become important features of our landscapes while others are likely long to remain rare and little known.

Rich as we Americans are in native maples we must turn to other parts of the world for some of the most desirable ornamental species, especially the dwarfer forms. Our own small members of this family—the Mountain, the Striped and the Western Dwarf Maples—have decided limitations for ornamental planting and are not to be compared with the Japanese Maples which have been developed into forms of great beauty by these nature-loving people. In fact Japan is said to be the ancestral home of the great Maple Family which still dominates the island forests. Two closely related species—*Acer palmatum* and *A. japonicum*—have been developed into more than a score of varieties, largely through the variations of the leaves. In the older types the leaves are broad with nearly a dozen pointed lobes and from this extreme there are all gradations to leaves cut into such narrow strips that the lobes seem little more than slender veins. There are also remarkable color variations, the prevailing tones being beautiful reds which attract admiring attention wherever they are seen. In Japan the festivals of the maples when the leaves reach their maximum of color in autumn are as popular as those of the cherry blossoms in spring. The Tartarian Maple (*Acer ginnala*) is another Oriental species, hardier than some of the Japanese forms and desirable for planting in shrubby borders or in more northern regions.

Another maple which may have originated in the Orient but has been

CONES AND LEAVES OF THE SMALL-FLOWERED JAPANESE PINE (PINUS PARVIFLORA)

naturalized in Europe since ancient times is the European Cork Maple—*Acer campestre*. This is an attractive, small tree, often branching to the ground, which is now offered by American nurseries for ornamental planting. There are several well-marked varieties.

The Japanese Empress Tree or Paulownia is an introduction from the Orient which is likely to become increasingly popular for ornamental planting. It can be grown as a permanent tree at least as far north as Philadelphia, making a fine showing in lawns, parks and home grounds both when in blossom in early spring and when in leaf throughout the summer. It can also be used to advantage in more northern regions as a quick-growing low screen, giving a tropical effect, by cutting off the trunk of the young tree at or near the ground to induce the sending up of a few large shoots that grow quickly and bear leaves of enormous size. The species is hardy enough for this sort of treatment as far north as Montreal.

This Empress Tree is one of the very few arborescent forms in the great Figwort Family. In most nursery catalogs and many books it is listed as *Paulownia imperialis* but the accepted technical name is now *P. tomentosa*. The tree is closely related to the catalpa and resembles the latter in many ways. The blossoms appear in spring before the leaves, being borne in large panicles, which are very suggestive of those of the catalpas, except for the blue of the corollas. After the blossoms fall the large leaves come out, most of them broadly ovate but some three-lobed. The ovaries develop into good-sized leathery capsules, which hang on in

LEAVES AND FRUIT OF THE SILVER BELL

autumn even after the leaves fall off and split open to let loose the winged seeds. Through the wide dispersal of these from trees in parks and home grounds the species has become naturalized in many of the South Atlantic and Southern States.

The Kadsura Tree is still another Japanese species which has been pronounced by experts as one of the most desirable introductions from those far-off islands. It rejoices in the technical name *Cercidiphyllum japonicum* but fortunately we can plant it and simply call it our Kadsura, which will at least enlist the interest of the neighbors. And as the tree grows rapidly into a beautiful pyramid of green in summer, that turns to lovely tones of gold and salmon-pink in autumn, their interest will change to admiration. When planted as a specimen it should not occupy the middle of the lawn but be placed in a less conspicuous position along the border. It requires ample room, however, as its wide-spreading branches come out close to the ground and often occupy a space two-thirds the height of the tree. It is better not to prune off these lower branches as their habit of growth makes the tree especially desirable as a background for the lawn.

Among the ornamental conifers an almost bewildering variety of foreign species are offered by the larger nurseries. Firs, spruces, hemlocks, arbor vitæ, cedars, cypresses and pines all have their representatives from the most remote regions of the globe. As we should expect from our experience with other plants some of the most distinctive of these come from Japan. Many people are familiar with pictures of Japanese landscapes to which the pine trees give such picturesque beauty. Some of the most attractive of these pines have been introduced into

SILVER BELL BLOSSOMS

America and are generally available for ornamental planting. The Japanese Red Pine is a tall species with bright green needles that grow in pairs. The Japanese Table Pine has the picturesque character of the pines commonly seen in Japanese gardens. It grows low in a spreading fashion that is most distinctive. The Small-flowered Japanese Pine (*Pinus parviflora*) is another fine species with five needles in a cluster and broad attractive cones of good size.

Besides these various trees from foreign soils, a few little-known American forms are coming into favor for ornamental planting. Many of these are more likely to be grown as shrubs than as trees but are beautiful in either condition.

The Silver Bell is perhaps the most beautiful of these American plants. It is more common as a shrub than as a tree and is becoming a favorite species for planting on lawns and home grounds in regions where the climate is not too severe. Being native to the great southern region from West Virginia to Texas it is hardy only as far north as Massachusetts.

The chief beauty of the Silver Bell lies in its pendent blossoms, which seem like snowdrops hung upon the twigs as the leaves unfold. The flowers are followed by the winged fruits, which remain on the tree a long time, nestling among the leaves. As an ornamental shrub for the lawn the Silver Bell has few equals.

SPRAY OF PURPLE BEECH—A VARIETY OF THE ENGLISH BEECH

The trees with colored foliage form another distinctive group which is receiving much attention for ornamental planting. It is very easy to set out too many trees of this type. One here and there to accentuate green backgrounds is much better than a dotting of them as isolated exclamation points all over the lawn. There are fine purples and reds in the special varieties of the maples, birches, beeches, plums and elms. The Purple Beech—a variety of the English beech—is one of the most desirable of these colored trees. There are also golden oaks and golden poplars which give a touch of color throughout the summer.

Trees for Streets and Avenues

Comparatively few trees meet all the requirements necessary to success for planting along the streets of modern cities. Such trees must be able to grow rapidly with comparatively little room for root development, and yet be so long-lived that they become fairly permanent. They must withstand the dust and gases from streets, houses and factories. They must be practically free from insect and fungous pests. And with all these characteristics they must have attractive compact outlines and give a dense shade.

Probably no tree more nearly meets these conditions than the Oriental Plane, which has been gaining rapidly in favor with the American public during

LEAVES AND SEED-BALL OF THE ORIENTAL PLANE

the last decade. It seems to be the ideal street tree, provided it has been properly trained when young so that it has a straight trunk. Care in the nursery is necessary for this result and cheaply grown trees are likely to be unsatisfactory as a consequence.

This Oriental Plane tree has been intimately associated with city dwellers for thousands of years and has remained in favor all the time. "This is the plane tree of the Greek writers," as Miss Rogers says, "in groves of which Plato walked and discoursed—a tree held in worshipful esteem for its stateliness and beauty. On occasions they poured wine upon its roots and decked its limbs with jewels and gold. Xerxes halted his unwieldy army for days that he might contemplate to his satisfaction the beauty of a single tree. He had its form wrought upon a medal of gold to help him to remember it the rest of his life." There are now standing in Europe some such plane trees whose age is estimated at something like four thousand years. Nearly three centuries ago John Parkinson, the famous herbalist, mentioned the fact that these planes were planted by waysides and in market places "for their shadowes sake only," and in America to-day this is a sufficient reason for adorning our streets with them.

The Oriental Plane is a more compact tree than its wide-spreading American cousin—our familiar sycamore. The latter soon becomes too large and spreads

FLOWERING BRANCH OF THE EUROPEAN LINDEN

too broadly to be well adapted to street planting. The leaves of the two are quite similar, those of the Oriental species being generally smaller and more uniform. The blossoms and seedballs are much alike in the two trees.

The European Linden is also becoming favorably known for street planting. At least three species and several varieties come under this general heading, the most desirable kind for avenue use being the typical form, called technically *Tilia vulgaris* or sometimes *Tilia europaea.* This species has the symmetrical outline so desirable for street use and makes a fine uniform showing when many are planted in a line. Fortunately the species is not yet largely used in America for clipping into formal outlines as it is in Europe, although there are places here where it might well be used as it is along the canal banks in Holland—the sides next the water being allowed to grow naturally and the half next the houses being sheared off. The other two species from Europe now offered by American nurseries—the Silver-leaved Linden and the Large-leaved Linden—are more desirable for use as individual specimens for parks and lawns than for street planting.

The Bolleana Poplar is another tree that should be more generally known. It is a fastigiate variety of the Silver Poplar just as the Lombardy is of the Italian Poplar. The habit of growth of Bolleana is a bit more spreading than the Lombardy and the foliage is more striking because of the white under surfaces of the leaves. While this variety has the faults of its family—rapid growth and quick decline, with some tendency to dying branches—it is worth planting to a limited extent in narrow streets and small home grounds where there is not room for spreading trees. It also can be combined to great advantage with the Lombardy Poplar in group plantings, and should be used occasionally to relieve the monotony of the endless stretches of Carolina Poplars which are so generally overplanted. The Bolleana Poplar is now offered by many nurseries, and it is an easy tree to grow from cuttings.

The Norway Maple has been planted so often and for so many years that it has sprung up naturally in many regions. It is treated of at some length upon a later page but should be mentioned in this connection as almost an ideal street tree for residence sections. It tends to form heads too low and as a result should be carefully pruned up when young. Its dense foliage, symmetrical outline and moderate size, as well as its freedom from enemies, help to make it a favorite in most cities. The tendency now is to overplant it, for a city should always have some variety, even in the shade trees along its streets.

LIST OF PLATES AND DESCRIPTIONS

OUR TREES
HOW TO KNOW THEM

THE WHITE PINE
PINUS STROBUS

THE WHITE PINE

IN many respects the White Pine is the most important timber tree which the American Continent has produced. It has been preëminently the tree producing lumber for building purposes, having the qualities that adapted it to a great variety of uses. During recent years the available supply has become more and more limited so that the price has rapidly risen and the lumber can no longer be used for many of the purposes to which it was formerly applied. Original forests of this tree are becoming more and more scarce and where they exist in centres of population they become a place of pilgrimage, as in the case of the famous White Pine grove at Carlisle, Massachusetts.

The White Pine has such distinctive characteristics that the tree is known to every one who has paid the slightest attention to the plant world. It is at once distinguished at a distance from the Norway Pine and the Pitch Pine by the comparative fineness of its foliage, the slender needles, arranged in clusters of five, being borne along the sides of comparatively slender branches that sweep out horizontally with their tips commonly curving upwards. As seen close at hand these needles show two or three distinct whitish lines on the lower surfaces as well as a very finely serrated margin. The young twigs are brownish, more or less covered with a fine pubescence, while the older twigs are smooth and shining. The cones are very characteristic, being long and comparatively slender, with their scales enlarged toward the outer end but rather thin at the tip. The winged seeds are light brown in color.

The White Pine is essentially a Northern tree, its original range extending from Newfoundland to Ontario and Southern Manitoba, thence going southward to Minnesota, Iowa, Michigan and Ohio, and following the Alleghany Mountains into Georgia. In many parts of this territory primeval forests of White Pine formerly covered vast areas, but these have been almost wholly cut down. Much attention has of late been given to reforesting some of these areas, and the White Pine is deservedly popular for forest planting as well as for use in landscape gardening. In areas protected from fire the species very often spreads naturally from seed trees, the seedlings getting a start in the shade of the Aspens and other trees that occur in abandoned pasture lands. In reforesting by man, however, it is better to set out nursery grown seedlings than to attempt to grow from seed sown on the land to be forested.

THE LONG-LEAVED PINE OR SOUTHERN YELLOW PINE

NO other conifer can compare with the Long-leaved Pine in the striking beauty of its foliage. The slender leaves in clusters of threes commonly reach a length of a foot or more, and give a distinctive effect to the branches of the tall trees which may be noted for a considerable distance; and the beauty of the trees when young is even greater. "Any one who has travelled south of Virginia," writes Mr. J. Horace McFarland, "cannot fail to have noted the lovely green leaf-fountains springing up from the ground along the railroads. These are the young trees of the Long-leaved or Southern Yellow Pine. How beautiful they are, these narrow leaves of vivid green, more than a foot long, drooping gracefully from the centre outward, with none of the stiffness of our Northern species. In some places they seem to fairly bubble in green from all the surface of the ground, so close are they. And the grand Long-leaved Pine itself, maintained in lusty vigor above these greeneries, is a tree of simple dignity, emphasized strongly when seen at its best either in the uncut forest or in a planted avenue." Of late years this species has served to satisfy the barbaric taste for dead greenery, the leaves being strung on threads and the branches and young trees being sent North in quantities for holiday decorations. It is to be hoped that this phase of our lack of civilization will pass before very long, for discriminating people will surely discern the folly of such practices.

As an economic tree the Long-leaved Pine is of first importance. The long, straight trunks are in great demand in shipbuilding and many other constructive enterprises; the yellow timber sawed into boards is one of the most important sources of our lumber supply; the resinous sap is the source of great quantities of turpentine and rosin; the leaves furnish by distillation an important essential oil and, by treatment with alkali, a "pine wool" that is utilized for various purposes.

The Long-leaved Pine is of comparatively limited distribution as a native tree. It is found from Virginia to Florida and west to the Mississippi River, although it also occurs locally in Texas. It is not hardy at the North. The cones are of large size, often nearly a foot long, each thickened scale being armed with a sharp recurved spine. Between these scales the seeds develop, each having a winged expansion about three-quarters of an inch long.

The Loblolly Pine, or Old-field Pine (*Pinus Tæda*), is another southern species ranging as far north as New Jersey which furnishes considerable yellow pine lumber The tree was formerly very abundant in the south.

LONG-LEAVED PINE — SOUTHERN YELLOW PINE

PINUS PALUSTRIS

PITCH PINE

PINUS RIGIDA

THE PITCH PINE

THE Pitch Pine is in every way a less valuable and a less attractive tree than the White Pine. As seen at a distance it has a much coarser appearance, a fact which is due to its larger leaves that are arranged in groups of threes along much thicker branches. The general color of the foliage is also lighter. As seen near at hand the leaves show narrow rows of white spots along the sides. The bark of the young branches is yellow brown, with no pubescent covering. The cones are large, and very much broader than those of the White Pine, the scales being armed with a stout, sharp spine at the middle of the outer margin. The cones remain upon the trees for several years after the winged seeds have been shed, so that one of the easiest ways to recognize the tree is to look for these broad, short cones hanging from the older branches.

The Pitch Pine seldom attains a height of more than forty or fifty feet, although occasionally taller specimens are found. In older trees many of the branches are likely to be wanting, so that the appearance lacks symmetry and grace. The bark of the trunk is thickly furrowed and more or less covered with rather large scales.

The Pitch Pine is remarkable for the large amount of resin produced upon the buds and branches. This fact doubtless led to the use of its common name as well as to the name Torch Pine, by which it is sometimes known. It is essentially a tree of sandy regions and occurs from New Brunswick to Ontario, south to Virginia and Kentucky and west to Ohio. It has not the advantages for planting, either in forestry or in landscape gardening, possessed by the White Pine.

The flowers of the Pitch Pine appear early in summer, the pollen-bearing blossoms being produced in great abundance at the base of the new season's growth. They are of a general reddish-yellow color. The seed-bearing flowers are produced along the sides of the new season's twigs, being arranged either singly or in clusters of two or more. The pollen-bearing flowers soon drop off, while the others slowly develop into cones, reaching maturity only at the end of the second season.

In the Pacific coast region from Oregon southward, an interesting pine somewhat similar to our eastern Pitch Pine occurs. It is called the Knob-cone Pine (*Pinus attenuata*), and is especially remarkable for the cones that remain upon the tree unopened for many years, even becoming imbedded in the branch without scattering the seeds. When the tree dies, or a fire sweeps through the forest, the seeds may be set free to start a new generation of trees.

THE RED PINE OR NORWAY PINE

THE Red Pine is one of the most majestic of all our Northern trees. It has a massive dignity that renders it more impressive than any of the other conifers growing in the same regions. The trunk is often of great height and large diameter, and the long, stout leaves give a suggestion of strength that is not so fully given by the White Pine or the Pitch Pine.

The three widely distributed native Pines of our Northern States are readily distinguished by the number of needles in a cluster. In the Red Pine there are two, in the Pitch Pine three, and in the White Pine five; consequently by this character alone one can always be sure of the species. Each pair of needles of the Red Pine is arranged in a rather long sheath at the base, the needles being four to six inches long and the sheaths often being an inch long. These leaves are generally clustered towards the ends of the branches and are dark green in color, more or less covered with a glaucous bloom. This coloring and arrangement of the foliage gives to those trees that grow in an open situation where there is opportunity for a symmetrical development of their branches, an appearance of great beauty which is enhanced to an extraordinary degree for a few days in early spring, when the red clusters of pollen-bearing flowers appear in enormous numbers on the tips of the branches. Vast quantities of pollen are developed from these flowers, to be carried through the air in every direction and often to float as a visible layer upon the surface of quiet waters. A small proportion of the pollen-grains serve to fertilize the ovules in the young cones on the ends of the branches. These cones require two years before they reach maturity, at which time they are generally ovate in shape and average about two inches in length. Their scales are thickened at the tip, but they have not the strong spines that distinguish the Pitch Pine, the cones of which are somewhat similar in general form.

This species is often called the Norway Pine and the Canadian Pine as well as the Red Pine, the latter name being due to the color of the bark of the trunk. It is essentially a tree of dry, sandy soils and is found from Newfoundland to the Gulf of St. Lawrence, west to Southern Manitoba and south to the more northern states, reaching Minnesota, Wisconsin, Northern Ohio, Pennsylvania, and Massachusetts.

The wood is less valuable than that of the White Pine, being generally of a light red color and weighing thirty pounds per cubic foot. It has not the lasting qualities out of doors of some of the other pines but is valuable for interior building purposes.

The Red Pine is valuable for planting as a landscape tree on account of its hardiness, beauty of foliage, and rapidity of growth. It may be propagated from seed, although it is not commonly offered for sale by nurserymen. Two or three year old seedlings are desirable for planting for forestry purposes.

RED PINE—NORWAY PINE

PINUS RESINOSA

GRAY PINE — JACK PINE

PINUS DIVARICATA

THE GRAY PINE OR JACK PINE

AN idea of the general appearance of this Pine as it grows toward the southern limit of its range may be obtained from the tree pictured on the plate. The bizarré scragginess so noticeable in isolated pines of other species seems here carried to an extreme and the tree has consequently a picturesque effect that seems well suited to the banks of northern lakes and rivers. For this is the most boreal of our native pines extending far toward the Arctic Circle and finding its southern limit in the northern New England states, Michigan, and Minnesota, though touching the northern counties of Illinois. A notable development of it occurs in the Jack Pine barrens of Michigan, but it is much farther north that it reaches its best estate. In the great region north of Lake Superior extending far up to the valleys of the Mackenzie and Athabasca Rivers it is an important timber tree reaching a height of seventy feet and yielding fuel and lumber where these are invaluable. In the more southern parts of its range it commonly occurs as a scrubby growth that is often of value as a nurse-crop for the other sorts of pines.

The distinguishing characters of the Gray Pine may be seen in the plate. The pairs of short, broad leaves of a gray-green color are thickly clustered on short branches. The pollen-bearing flowers encircle the twigs at the base of the new season's growth, while the stemless cones are pointed and conical or oblong, and generally more or less curved; they are held erect on the branch, and are seldom more than two inches long. As in the case of the Pitch Pine these cones remain upon the branches for years after the seeds have been scattered from them, and their presence adds to the characteristic appearance of the trees.

The Jack Pine is recommended by the Forest service for planting in regions where better trees cannot be grown. It serves well in the Dakotas and the sandy regions of the North Central states for wind-breaks and shelter belts. It is very hardy and thrifty under adverse conditions of soil and moisture.

An interesting division of the native pines is made by Professor Sargent in his "Manual of the Trees of North America:" twelve species are classified as Soft Pines, and the other twenty-two species as Pitch Pines. The characteristics of the Soft Pines are given in these words: "Wood soft, close-grained, light colored, the sapwood thin and nearly white; sheaths of the leaf-clusters deciduous; leaves with one fibro-vascular bundle." The White Pine is a typical example of this group. The characteristics of the Pitch Pines are given in these words: " Wood usually heavy, coarse-grained, generally dark colored, with pale often thick sapwood; cones green at maturity, becoming various shades of brown; cone-scales more or less thickened, mostly armed; seeds shorter than their wings; leaves with two fibro-vascular bundles." The Pitch Pine is a typical example of this group.

THE JERSEY PINE OR SCRUB PINE

ALONG the Atlantic coast from New York to Georgia another scrub pine occurs which is often called the Jersey Pine because it is the species found in the pine barrens along the New Jersey shore. Technically it is known as *Pinus Virginiana* In several respects it resembles the Jack Pine: the pairs of gray-green leaves are short and stout and the manner of growth is scrubby, but the scales of the cones are armed with short spines, a fact which at once differentiates this species from the Jack Pine.

In the East the Jersey Pine seldom reaches a height greater than forty feet or a trunk diameter greater than eighteen inches, but in the Middle West, especially in Indiana and Kentucky, it often attains to twice these proportions. It has comparatively little economic value, though it doubtless serves a very useful purpose in helping to hold in place the barren sandy soils in which it grows, as well as in serving as a cover crop to get other trees started.

There are also numerous other pines of more or less limited distribution in various parts of America; thirty-four species of native American trees are credited to the genus Pinus in Sargent's Manual of Trees. Aside from those which have already been treated of, the most important of these, perhaps, is the Yellow Pine or Short-leaved Pine (*Pinus echinata*) which during recent years has furnished a vast quantity of lumber. This tree is native to most of the Southern States, and extends as far north as New York and as far west as Texas. It commonly reaches a height of one hundred feet and a trunk diameter of four feet, so that it is very valuable as a timber tree.

Another important timber species is the Western Yellow Pine (*Pinus ponderosa*) which ranges over the great region of the United States west of the one hundredth meridian. Along the western side of the Sierra Mountains the trees often reach a height of two hundred feet and a trunk diameter of six feet. It is a desirable tree for forestry purposes in the west.

For ornamental purposes the pines have various uses. The taller species serve to give a picturesque effect to the landscape, and may be planted on barren upland soil in which many other trees are not likely to thrive. The long tap-roots of the pines, which enable them to thrive on dry soils because the roots go down for water, render them more difficult to transplant than many sorts of trees, and therefore nursery-grown specimens are desirable. There are a number of spreading shrub-like pines which are useful for filling in underwoods or for planting along borders; probably the best of these is the Swiss Mountain Pine, some varieties of which have a wide spreading habit.

JERSEY PINE — SCRUB PINE
PINUS VIRGINIANA

SCOTCH PINE
PINUS SYLVESTRIS

THE SCOTCH PINE

I T is said that the Scotch Pine is the only conifer native to Scotland and England, and that this may be the reason why the tree is very commonly called the Scotch Fir in Great Britain. It is a typical Pine, rather than a Fir, and the latter name was probably applied to it centuries ago, before the Firs had generally been introduced into Great Britain. In America the species has been very commonly planted in the past as an ornamental tree, but is is not so popular now for this purpose, as experience has shown that it is a short-lived tree, rather more subject to attack by insects than some of our native species.

In its general aspect, as seen at a little distance, the Scotch Pine bears a resemblance to our native Pitch Pine, although it seems somewhat less rugged. Drawing nearer, one finds the rather short leaves smoother than those of the Pitch Pine, and arranged in pairs instead of in groups of three. The bark of the twigs is also darker and the needles themselves are not so stout. The cones when closed are longer and more slender than those of the Pitch Pine, although there is a resemblance in the shape of the exposed parts of the scales. They are ovate, or conical, and about an inch long. When open they have a rather shapeless appearance. The general color of the foliage is slightly yellow green. In England there is a horticultural variety in which the foliage changes to a golden color in winter, although it is green at other seasons. The English people have shown great wisdom in planting this and other species of evergreens, and various other trees and shrubs, for the especial purpose of getting beautiful landscape effects during the winter months. Much attention has been paid to these winter gardens, and special lists have been made of species which will give attractive displays during each of the months from November to March.

The Scotch Pine is found not only in Great Britain but throughout Northern Europe and over much of Asia, being the chief timber pine of a vast region in the Eastern Continent. This species has for many centuries furnished the masts for the ships of Europe and is said to have been preferred for this purpose by English shipbuilders to any of the American Pines. In his "Trees and Shrubs of Massachusetts" George B. Emerson wrote that he had for many years cultivated the Scotch Pine on the very exposed part of the coast of Boston Bay, and had found it "hardier, of more rapid growth, and less needing protection than either of our Massachusetts Pines." This was written many years ago, and it would be interesting to know the later history of these trees. The Forest service recommends this species for planting in the Prairie States on account of its ability to grow in dry regions.

THE AUSTRIAN PINE

ONE who is familiar with our native Red Pine will readily see striking resemblances between this species and the Austrian Pine. The paired leaves are almost identical in shape and size, as well as in their manner of growth along the branches. The cones of the Austrian species are somewhat the larger and slightly different in shape, this being perhaps the most striking peculiarity which distinguishes the two. The Austrian Pine is a mountainous species from eastern Europe and was one of the earliest foreign evergreens to be introduced into America, being for many years largely planted in parks and private grounds as an ornamental tree. It has many advantages for this purpose, being hardy and resistant to extremes of temperature, growing fairly rapidly, and being easily obtainable from nurserymen. It should not, however, supplant our native species to too great an extent. It lacks the grace and beauty of the White Pine and seldom attains the majestic appearance of the Red Pine.

The needles of the Austrian Pine are commonly about four inches long, with a shiny dark-green surface, slightly lighter colored acute points, and a sheath at the base about a quarter of an inch in length. The terminal buds have a long, acuminate point and two or three rows of basal scales which have long, curiously-fringed tips that project nearly at right angles in a most characteristic fashion, forming, in fact, a rosette around the lower half of the bud. The bark of the latest season's shoots is greenish brown, while the sheaths around the bases of the needles are of a distinct gray color. The cones vary in length from an inch and a half to two inches, are generally rather ovate when closed, and have much of the ends of the scales exposed to view. They remain upon the tree for several years and generally do not open until two years after they have reached full size. On the accompanying plate the abundant masses of pollen-bearing flowers are shown next to the cone, while next to these may be seen the seed-bearing flowers upon the tip of the new shoot. The species is also sometimes called the Black Pine.

Botanically the Austrian Pine is a variety of that Corsican Pine (*Pinus Laricio*) being distinguished by its dark-green rigid leaves and its grayish-brown twigs. There are four other varieties of Corsican Pine recommended for landscape planting, all being notable for rapidity of growth and darkness of foliage. One of the most interesting is the Pygmy Pine (var. *pygmata*) which is a bushy pine.

(26)

AUSTRIAN PINE

PINUS AUSTRIACA

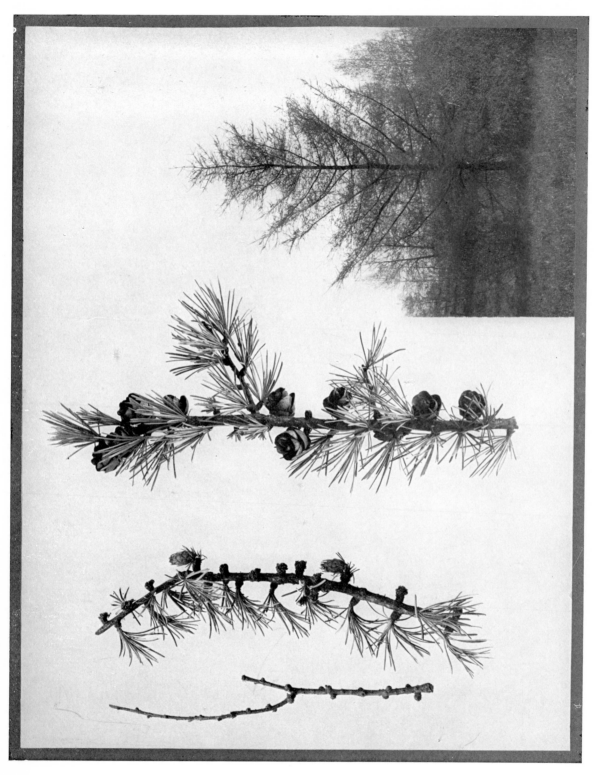

AMERICAN LARCH – TAMARACK

LARIX AMERICANA

THE AMERICAN LARCH OR TAMARACK

THE American Larch, often called also Tamarack or Hacmatac, is especially notable because it is a deciduous conifer, the leaves falling off every autumn. Like all the Larches, the small needle-shaped leaves are borne in dense clusters at the tips of very short branches. This gives to the foliage of the tree a distinctive appearance which enables one to distinguish it at a distance, even in summer, from any of our other native conifers. On the approach of autumn the dark green leaves change to a pale yellow and later fall to the ground, this generally taking place during October.

The Tamarack is essentially a tree of the cold North, ranging from the Arctic Circle south to Pennsylvania, Indiana, Illinois, and Minnesota. It is one of the most characteristic trees of lowland swamps, forming in many localities extensive forests. It is occasionally found growing on higher lands, but seems to thrive most successfully in wet situations.

The long, fibrous roots of the trees growing in the swamps were used by the Indians in making their birch-bark canoes, a fact of which Longfellow made mention in the well-known lines in "Hiawatha:"

> "Give me of your roots, O Tamarack!
> Of your fibrous roots, O Larch Tree!
> My canoe to bind together,
> So to bind the ends together
> That the water may not enter,
> That the river may not wet me!"

The Tamarack blossoms very early in spring, generally during the last week in March or the first two weeks in April. The seed-bearing flowers are of a beautiful deep red color, which is one of the most brilliant and characteristic hues to be found in the spring forest. These seed-bearing flowers are erect at the tips of short branches. The cones are short and broad, and not nearly so attractive in form as those of the European Larch or the Spruces and the Pines. These cones remain upon the tree for a year or more after they have shed the small winged seeds.

In the more northern parts of its range the Tamarack is much more likely to grow on well-drained uplands than in New England. It commonly attains a height of fifty or sixty feet and a trunk diameter of about eighteen inches, being a straight, slender tree of decided beauty when growing in the open. In the North it is useful for ornamental planting, taking on as it matures more picturesque shapes than the European Larches. It thrives, as one would expect, better in moist than in dry situations, and it should be transplanted either in autumn after the leaves have fallen or very early in spring before the young leaves begin to develop.

In the Northwest the Western Larch (*Larix occidentalis*) is an important timber tree reaching a height of two hundred and fifty feet, and furnishing lumber of great value for many purposes. It is one of the most splendid trees of all the tribe of conifers.

THE EUROPEAN LARCH

THE European Larch is justly one of the favorite conifers for ornamental planting. It is a beautiful tree, having an extraordinary grace of outline, with pendent branchlets clothed through the summer with delicate tufts of slender leaves of a green that varies from the lightest tints in early spring to the deep green of summer and the yellow green and green yellow of autumn. Even after the leaves have fallen the tree has a certain grace that renders it attractive through the winter, the drooping branches being studded along their sides by short projections, from the ends of which the leaves arise, as well as here and there by the interesting upright cones of a form and size much more attractive than the cones of the American Larch.

A little study of the branch shown at the right of the middle on the plate will give a definite knowledge of the conditions of blossoming of this Larch. Along the left-hand side of the twig are numerous fascicles of leaves just beginning to push out, and at the bottom on the same side of the twig there is a cluster of the pollen-bearing flowers. On the opposite side the most conspicuous features are the two large clusters of seed-bearing blossoms arising from a nest of developing leaves. By a comparison of these two sets of flowers with the two cones shown in the picture at the left, one can readily see that the former will develop into cones like the latter.

According to Mrs. Dyson the native home of this Larch "is on the snow mountains of Germany, Austria and Italy. It climbs higher than the Silver Fir, as high as the Norway Spruce; but the Spruce seems to like best the side of the mountain looking toward the north and the Larch prefers the brighter southern side."

The cones do not remain upon the trees so long after shedding the seeds as do those of the Tamarack, and the tree is much better adapted to comparatively dry soils than is the latter. For ornamental planting the European species has many advantages, not the least of which is that it may almost always be obtained of nurserymen in any desired quantity and at comparatively little expense. It is also a promising tree for forestry purposes as far west as the Dakotas and Nebraska. The trees thrive best in deep, light, well-drained soil in which the long roots may penetrate deeply. It is better to plant these Larches for forest purposes along with other trees like Chestnut, Ash, Elm, Pine, or Spruce. Two year old trees from the nursery are of best size for planting.

EUROPEAN LARCH

LARIX EUROPÆA

BLACK SPRUCE

PICEA MARIANA — PICEA NIGRA

THE BLACK SPRUCE

THE Black Spruce is easily distinguished among our native Spruces by the fact that the cones hang on the trees for years after they have dropped their seeds. It is also readily known from the White Spruce by the fact that there are fine hairs upon the young branches, and from the Red Spruce by the very different appearance of the cones, these averaging much larger in the latter species.

The Black Spruce is essentially a Northern tree, forming great areas of forest in the Far North, and in the more southern portions of its range forming the predominant element of the arboreal growth in those Spruce swamps which are so common in Southern Canada and the more northern states. It ranges from Newfoundland to Hudson Bay and northwestward, and extends southward to Minnesota, Wisconsin, Michigan, and Pennsylvania. Along the sides of the Alleghany Mountains it also ranges south to Virginia, extending farther south than either of the other spruces. It is the prevailing spruce in Eastern Massachusetts, where a glaucous form is sometimes found that might be mistaken for the White Spruce.

The young branches of the Black Spruce have the bark covered with small brownish or whitish hairs, which are readily seen with a hand-lens. The leaves encircle the young twig, and their average length is one-third of an inch. In cross section they are obtusely four-angled and at the tip they are acutely pointed. The branches in older trees are likely to be very irregular in their manner of growth, some of them projecting straight outward, others projecting downward near the trunk and upward toward their tips, a condition that is well shown in the tree illustrated on the plate. The ovate, reddish-brown buds are generally arranged in groups of three on the ends of the more vigorous branches. The cones vary from three-fourths of an inch to an inch and a half in height, being oval in general outline and having irregular teeth along the margins of the scales, one of the characters by which this species is distinguished from the Red Spruce. As stated above, these cones remain upon the trees for several years after maturing.

The wood of the Black Spruce is soft and light, weighing but twenty-eight pounds per cubic foot, and is chiefly of value for fuel and paper pulp, being rather extensively used for the latter purpose along with the other Spruces. This species is not desirable as an ornamental tree on account of the scraggly appearance of the larger trees in the more southern parts of its range, as well as the fact that it generally lives but a short time when planted for landscape purposes.

THE RED SPRUCE

IN Northern New England and much of Canada the Red Spruce is one of the most important timber trees, covering the mountain sides over great areas. It furnishes the chief soft wood from which paper pulp is manufactured and vast tracts of it have lately been set aside by the great paper companies in order that the supply of wood might be continuous and permanent. It is not a very desirable tree for ornamental planting, but it is extremely valuable for use in extensive forest systems that take advantage of the natural growth over large areas.

The yellow-green leaves of the Red Spruce are generally rather short, being less than half an inch long and obtusely pointed, with longitudinal rows of white dots along the sides. The surface of the bark of the youngest shoots is deep brownish red and is quite densely covered with stout brownish or blackish hairs. The bark of older branches is much darker, especially where most exposed to the weather. The reddish-brown buds are hairy, and the bark of the trunk on trees of good size is of a somewhat reddish color and more or less covered with thin scales.

The blossoms of the Red Spruce appear in May, the pollen-bearing flowers being short, cylindrical masses with reddish anthers, and the seed-bearing having purplish scales that give them an interesting appearance. When the cones mature they are generally from one to two inches long, oval in outline with the imbricated scales having slightly irregular margins. They begin to fall from the tree the first season as soon as they shed the small dark-brown winged seeds, and continue to drop off through the winter and spring, so that by the following summer they are practically all off the tree. This is one character by which the Red Spruce is easily distinguished from the Black Spruce.

The wood of the Red Spruce is rather light, weighing but twenty-eight pounds per cubic foot. It is soft and weak, but is largely manufactured into shingles and lumber. The tree grows chiefly on uplands, and extends southward to Massachusetts and New York and along the higher parts of the Alleghany Mountains to North Carolina.

During recent years the Colorado Blue Spruce (*Picea Parryana*) has become one of the most popular evergreens for ornamental planting. It is native to regions in Colorado, Utah and Wyoming where it grows at elevations between six thousand and ten thousand feet above sea level. The full-sized trees are generally about one hundred feet high.

RED SPRUCE
PICEA RUBENS

WHITE SPRUCE
PICEA CANADENSIS

THE WHITE SPRUCE

THE White Spruce is one of the most magnificent evergreens native to North America. When growing in the open it is a beautiful, symmetrical tree, thickly clothed with branches but having a tufted appearance that distinguishes it at a glance from the Norway Spruce. Close at hand the branches are at once separated from those of the Red Spruce and the Black Spruce by the fact that, while the bark of the young twigs of the two latter species are both rather thickly covered with hairs, the bark of the young twigs of the White Spruce is glabrous, lacking these hairs. It may also often be distinguished by the fact that the leaves, especially when bruised, have a rather unpleasant odor, as well as by their whitish color which gives the tree its common name.

Like the other spruces this is a Northern species, ranging from Newfoundland to Alaska and extending southward to the northern tier of states and British Columbia. Throughout this vast range it grows with the other Spruces and by many lumbermen is not distinguished from them. It is especially abundant along the coast of Maine. In the more northern regions the trees sometimes reach a height of a hundred and fifty feet and a trunk diameter of four feet, but commonly in more southern localities it reaches a height of but sixty feet and a trunk diameter of two feet. The bark of the latest season's shoots is generally reddish brown, while that of older branches is much darker. The leaves are about four-fifths of an inch long, with sharply pointed tips, and stripes of white dots on each of the four sides. The cones are borne on the tips of the smaller twigs and when fully developed are of an average length of one and a half inches. The margins of the scales are thin and rounded, the middle of the margin being commonly truncate and generally entire. The small seeds with the wing attached are about a quarter of an inch long. The cones drop off after the seeds are shed, and may generally be found beneath the tree at any season of the year.

The wood of the White Spruce is light in color, soft and weak, weighing but twenty-five pounds per cubic foot. It is extensively used in the making of lumber and in the manufacture of paper pulp. In Canada and the extreme Northern States this is one of the most desirable evergreens for ornamental planting, but further south it is not adapted to the climate and becomes unsightly as it grows older.

The Western White Spruce or Engelmann's Spruce (*Picea Engelmanni*) is a splendid tree that forms mountain forests from British Columbia southward. It seems to grow naturally only at an elevation of at least a mile, although it thrives as an ornamental tree near sea level in the Eastern States. Its chief objection for this purpose is found in the disagreeable odor of the leaves.

THE NORWAY SPRUCE

OF all introduced evergreen trees the Norway Spruce has been more generally planted for landscape purposes than any other. For many years it was almost the only evergreen offered by nurserymen for general planting, and it had many qualities which made it desirable for this purpose. It is of rapid, symmetrical growth, keeping its foliage on the lower as well as the upper branches, and developing cones of large size and beautiful form, which add to the attractiveness of the upper part of the tree. Having developed in the rigorous climate of Northern Europe it is hardy in all situations and is free from attack by insect and fungus enemies.

The Norway Spruce is at once distinguished from all our native Spruces by its slender cones, which are three to six inches long and one or two inches broad. The margins of the scales are rather thin, being slightly and irregularly toothed, and the small winged seed that escape from the scales being about one-third of an inch long. The bark of the young twigs is of a light reddish-brown color, while that of the older branches is much darker. The buds are nearly conical in form and have reddish-brown, imbricated scales.

As the Red Spruce is the prevailing tree on the New England mountains, so the Norway Spruce is the prevailing tree in the Alps, where in the great forests on the mountain-sides individual trees sometimes reach a height of one hundred and fifty feet. The wood of this species forms the white Deal of the European lumber-market, holding much the same place that the White Pine has held in the American lumber-market. From the resin of this tree Burgundy pitch is manufactured.

While it is probable that in the future the Norway Spruce will not hold the almost exclusive place in landscape planting that it has held in the past, it is likely to remain one of the most important evergreen trees for this purpose. It is easily obtained from nurserymen, and has many advantages over other species for the planting of hedges and in groups where symmetry of growth is especially desired. There also seems to be a great future for it as a forest tree in America, as it is stated by the Forest Service to be in every way superior to our native spruces for reforesting the great tracts of timber land in the Northeast region as well as along the mountains Southward. It does not thrive in the plains region of the West. The trees grow more rapidly than those of the Red Spruce or the White Spruce. There are a great many horticultural varieties recommended for ornamental planting.

NORWAY SPRUCE
PICEA EXCELSA

HEMLOCK
TSUGA CANADENSIS

THE HEMLOCK

THE Hemlock is one of the most beautiful and best known of our native conifers. On account of its slender twigs and small, flattened leaves it has a grace of growth, especially when young, which is lacking in most of the evergreens. It is an abundant and characteristic feature in nearly all our Northern forests, ranging from Nova Scotia to Michigan, Wisconsin, and Minnesota, on the north, and extending southward along the mountain slopes to Alabama and Georgia. The smaller branches have a flattened appearance, due largely to the two-ranked arrangement of the leaves along each side. One of the most characteristic features is to be found in the row of leaves along the top of the branch, extending in the same direction as the twig and commonly lying flat upon it. The leaves in this top row are usually but about half the length of the main series of leaves along the sides. The latter are commonly about half an inch long and each leaf has a very short petiole, which is also a distinguishing feature of the Hemlock. The leaves are bright shining green on their upper surfaces and much lighter on the under surface, this latter effect being chiefly due to the whitish stripes along and beside the midrib. When rubbed together in the hands the leaves have a slightly resinous odor.

The Hemlock is beautiful at any season of the year, but it has an especial charm just as the new growth has developed on the ends of the twigs in early summer, each young branch being of a beautiful light green color that forms a charming harmony with the dark rich green of the rest of the branches. These variegated sprays of the Hemlock give to the underwoods in June one of their most distinctive attractions.

The Hemlock comes into blossom rather early in the spring. The masses of staminate flowers are shown on the twig at the extreme left of the plate, while the cone-like, seed-bearing flowers are shown on the next twig. The latter develop during the same season into the rather small cones of a red-brown color, which generally do not fall off until the following spring. In the forest the Hemlock trees attain a large size and furnish lumber useful for many purposes. The tree is also valuable for ornamental planting, having been developed by horticultural art into a great variety of forms which are offered by nurserymen.

The Carolina Hemlock (*Tsuga Caroliniana*) is a more graceful species than its northern cousin, and is coming rapidly into favor for ornamental planting. It is generally to be distinguished by its longer, darker green leaves with entire margins; the cone-scales are oblong. In Alaska and the far Northwest there are two other species of Hemlock, both of which have been utilized for landscape planting in Europe.

THE BALSAM FIR

IT is probably on account of the interesting psychological fact of the curious association of the sense of smell with the memory of former experiences that the Balsam
Fir holds a unique position among the evergreens in the minds of most people who
have lived for a time in the region where it grows. The delightful odor of the leaves is
sure to recall to these fortunate ones, experiences of outings in the forests or of balsam
pillows carried to village or city homes. The odor certainly is one of the most refreshing
fragrances in Nature's pharmacy, and it seems fitting that the tree should also furnish,
through the unique reservoirs that stand out on the bark of the trunk and larger branches,
an abundant supply of one of the most potent medicines for the ills of throat and lungs.
This clear balsam is often used as medicine directly from the tree in the regions where it
grows. It is also largely used in preserving microscopic preparations and for various other
purposes.

The Balsam Fir may generally be distinguished at the first glance by the flattened
appearance of the horizontal branches, an appearance which is due to the usually horizontal position of the leaves, the upper surfaces of which are a bright, clear, green color
while the under surfaces are bluish green. The young shoots have the reddish-brown
bark clothed with stiff brown hairs. The reddish-brown buds have the scales covered by
a transparent, shining varnish. In addition to their balsamic odor the leaves have a distinct aromatic taste. As is well shown on the plate, the rather large cones project upward
from the smaller branches. These cones are generally about four inches long by one inch
in diameter and have scales with rounded margins.

The Balsam Fir is essentially a tree of the great northern forests, ranging as far
south as Pennsylvania, Michigan, and Minnesota, and along the higher slopes of the mountains to Virginia. It is a beautiful tree for ornamental planting in the regions where it is
found as a native, but farther south it is not so likely to thrive.

At least eight other species of Firs are found in North America. Most of these are
native to the far West, but one, Fraser's Fir (*Abies Fraseri*), is found well up along the
Appalachian Mountains in Virginia, North Carolina and Tennessee. It is generally a low
tree, rarely reaching a height of seventy feet even in its native home, and has little
value for landscape planting. The other species are commonly called White Firs, Red
Firs or Silver Firs. Several of them have been utilized for ornamental planting in Europe.

REDWOOD

PINE FAMILY

THE REDWOOD

TWO sister species of giant trees occupy a position unique among living plants: they are the oldest of living things; one is the tallest of living things; the other is the largest of living things; both are among the few surviving relics of a former geologic period; and each is now found only in comparatively limited areas on the Pacific slope. These two trees are, of course, the Redwood and the Big Tree; both belong to the genus Sequoia and are sometimes called by that name. The Redwood is *S. sempervirens* and the Big Tree is *S. Wellingtonia*. The former is found in a narrow strip of land near the coast in Oregon and Northern California, and does not grow at an altitude greater than three thousand feet; the latter is found in California on the slopes of the Sierra Nevada Mountains, at altitudes ranging from five thousand to eight thousand feet.

The specific characteristics of the Redwood are shown on the plate: an important distinction between this tree and the Big Tree is that the Redwood has two forms of leaves, with scaly buds and cones that mature in a single season; in the Big Tree there is but one kind of leaf, the buds are naked, and the cones require two seasons to mature. Well-developed Redwood trees in favorable situations reach a diameter of twenty feet and a height of three hundred and fifty feet, the tallest of known trees. The largest Big Trees have a diameter of thirty-four feet and a height nearly equal to that of the tallest Redwoods.

An interesting fact concerning the Redwood is its relation to the sea-fogs blown landward from the Pacific Ocean. "While moisture of the soil affects the development of the Redwood," writes Mr. Richard T. Fisher, "moisture of the atmosphere regulates its distribution. The limits of the sea-fogs are just about the limits of the tree. The fogs, unless scattered by the winds, flow inward among the mountains. Western exposures receive most of the mist they carry, except those higher ridges above their reach, which support in consequence only a scattering growth of Redwood. Eastern and southern slopes, where the sun is hot and the mists strike only occasionally, show few Redwoods, and these are short and limby."

Of the Big Trees another writer in the Bureau of Forestry says: "The Big Trees are unique in the world—the grandest, the largest, the oldest, the most majestically graceful of trees—and if it were not enough to be all this, they are among the scarcest of known tree species and have the extreme scientific value of being the best living representatives of a former geologic age. It is a tree which has come down to us through the vicissitudes of many centuries solely because of its superb qualifications."

No other trees in the world have excited so much comment nor attracted so many visitors. And all who see them agree that it is impossible to exaggerate their grandeur or to get an adequate conception of their majestic proportions without actually seeing them. It is fortunate indeed that these trees are now under the protection of the government and are to be preserved for future generations.

THE BALD CYPRESS

THE Bald Cypress is likely to be familiar to anyone who has lived in the great Atlantic Coast region between Delaware on the north and east and Texas on the south and west. For the Cypress swamps are a characteristic feature of this great region, and the trees which give the swamps their name are so distinctive that they are likely to attract the notice of every observer. The distinctive features of the trees are found in their ability to grow in submerged soil, in their curious buttressed bases with fluted outlines, in the strange "knees" sent up above the water by the great horizontal roots, in the small leaves arising from short branches—the leaves not only being deciduous themselves but generally taking with them when they fall the short branches on which they are borne—and in the interesting round and roughened cones. Of all these characteristics perhaps the "knees" are the most fascinating to the student: these knees rise several feet above the water by the abrupt upward bending of the main roots. While the botanists are not agreed as to the precise function of these knees, they seem to incline to the opinion that they have to do with an effort to get air, such knees being especially developed when the roots are under water. A recent observer states that in one case he saw a tree whose roots had been freed from earth by floods and that the tips were against solid rock so that the knees were formed by buckling upward as the tips grew.

During recent years the cypress swamps have become of great value as sources of lumber, the light soft wood being useful for many purposes, especially where resistance to moisture is necessary. The old trees are generally ragged and unsymmetrical, but young trees are of a beautiful pyramidal symmetry that makes them very desirable for ornamental planting. They thrive best in rather moist soil, but will grow in drier situations There is one native variety with needle-shaped leaves to which the name *imbricaria* has been given; and there are a number of horticultural varieties that are available for ornamental planting. The most popular of these is a weeping form.

The panicles of pollen-bearing flowers are shown in the middle picture of the plate. They mature in early spring, becoming of a purplish color and producing enormous quantities of pollen, which is wafted through the air to fertilize the small seed-bearing flowers on the ends of the twigs.

The Bald Cypress commonly occurs throughout most of the Southern States, extending northward to Ohio, Indiana, and Illinois, and being hardy when planted as far north as New England.

BALD CYPRESS
TAXODIUM DISTICHUM

CONIFERÆ

ARBOR VITÆ
THUYA OCCIDENTALIS

PINE FAMILY

THE ARBOR VITÆ

TO most Americans the Arbor Vitæ is familiar chiefly as a hedge plant, it being perhaps more generally grown for this purpose than any other tree. It is one of the most easily recognized of the evergreens on account of its flattened, frond-like branches, which led the Indians to call it the Feather-leaf. It is essentially a Northern form, being found in great abundance in the more northern parts of the American Continent, extending south to New England, Michigan, and Illinois, and on the elevations of the Alleghany Mountains to Virginia and Tennessee. It grows in greatest abundance in cold swamps, where it often forms the chief forest element, reaching a height of sixty feet and a diameter of two or three feet. The trunk is short and often split near its base into two or three parts. The soft, coarse-grained wood is light brown in color and weighs but twenty pounds per cubic foot. It is used in making shingles and railway-ties.

The leaves of the Arbor Vitæ are very small and much flattened, being suggestive of closely appressed, imbricated scales. They are arranged in opposite pairs, each succeeding pair alternating around the stem with the last. On the back of each leaf there is generally a small gland, which probably serves to give to the twigs their characteristic aromatic odor, which is especially evident when the leaves are bruised.

The flowers of the Arbor Vitæ appear in spring on the ends of the branches, the pollen-bearing and the seed-bearing blossoms being generally on the same plant. They are succeeded by small, cone-like fruits, each with six to twelve brown scales between which the small winged seeds are developed. These cones are rather inconspicuous and not very attractive in form. Some of them are shown near the middle of the accompanying plate.

The Arbor Vitæ has been so extensively planted that a great many horticultural forms have developed. These forms vary chiefly as to habit of growth and color of foliage. The species is deservedly popular in landscape planting, and although it grows rather slowly it is one of the most satisfactory evergreens for hedges and other ornamental purposes.

In the Pacific Coast region the Western Arbor Vitæ which is often locally called Red Cedar or Canoe Cedar is an abundant species. Its cone generally has six fertile scales while the cone of the eastern form has but four. "From this tree," writes Professor Sargent, "the Indians of the Northwest coast split the planks used in the construction of their lodges, carved the totems which decorate their villages, and hollowed out their great war canoes; and from the fibres of the inner bark made ropes, blankets, and thatch for their cabins." Technically the species is called *Thuya plicata*.

THE WHITE CEDAR

SOME confusion is caused in the identification of this species by the fact that in many regions the Arbor Vitæ is commonly known as the White Cedar. It is desirable that the Arbor Vitæ should be universally called by that distinctive and pleasing name, so that the White Cedar should not be confused with it. The latter species has a much more limited range than the former, being found chiefly along the Atlantic coast from Southern Maine to Northern Florida and not extending very far inland. It is essentially a swamp species, flourishing best where its roots are in water a large part of the year. It is doubtless on this account that the wood is able to withstand the injurious effect of contact with moist soil to a most extraordinary degree, a quality which renders it of great value for fence-posts and railway-ties, and which also gives an especial permanence to shingles made from cedar logs.

The White Cedar is very easily distinguished from the Arbor Vitæ by its cones, which are globular and brownish purple, being generally less than half an inch in diameter and having thickened scales that open on the inside and bear several small, winged seeds under each scale. The leaves are very small and scale-like, borne in opposite pairs which alternate along the twigs in a way to give a four-ranked appearance. On the middle of the back of most of the scales there is a rounded greenish gland.

The manner of growth of the White Cedar is very much more spreading and diffuse than that of the Red Cedar. Consequently it is not so attractive a tree for general planting, especially as there is a tendency for the lower branches to become **bare and scraggy** when the trees get older. The species may sometimes be utilized, however, in ornamental planting in wet places where it is difficult to get other trees to thrive.

In the far Western States occur two other species of the genus to which the White Cedar belongs. One of these is called the Yellow Cypress or Sitka Cypress (*Chamæcyparis Nootkatensis*) and occurs from Alaska southward to Oregon and Washington. The other is called the Lawson Cypress or Port Orford Cedar (*C. Lawsoniana*) and occurs in Oregon and California. There are a great many horticultural forms of each of these species which have long been in cultivation both in Europe and America.

RED CEDAR — SAVIN

PINE FAMILY

THE RED CEDAR OR SAVIN

THE Red Cedar is one of the most abundant and characteristic evergreen trees of eastern North America. As the species is now limited by the authorities it is distributed from Nova Scotia to New Brunswick, south to Georgia, Alabama and Texas, and west to Kansas, Nebraska, and Dakota. The tree has a characteristic columnar appearance, which is shown in the specimen illustrated on the plate, and when growing singly or in small groups along hillsides it forms one of the most distinctive and characteristic features of many landscapes, the natural plantings often giving to abandoned pastures a park-like effect which is exceedingly attractive. In some of the Southern States low hills are often covered with these trees almost to the exclusion of other species. Upon rare occasions trees have been found one hundred feet high but much more commonly they attain less than half this height, and the great majority of those which one sees are still smaller.

The wood of this tree has been an important commercial product. It is especially noted for its ability to resist the effects of moisture, which has led to its being largely used for fence-posts and the sills of buildings. It is also notable for its fragrance, which has been supposed to help in preventing the attacks of moths upon furs and woollen garments, and in consequence the wood is much used for closets and chests for preserving apparel. Cedar wood is also utilized for making lead pencils and various kinds of woodenware, as well as for the interior finish of houses and in ship building.

The branches of the Red Cedar are remarkable for the two forms of leaves which they bear. The most abundant kind of leaves are those which are small and scale-like, each leaf being acutely pointed and sub-triangular in shape. The other form is long and more or less needle-like, and it seems to be most often present upon branches which have grown rapidly. These two forms may be seen in the branches figured upon the plate. The berry-like fruits of the Red Cedar are known to every country dweller, being small bluish objects about the size of a pea, in which the thickened outer scales have grown together to enclose the three or four seeds. These cedar-berries are freely eaten by a great variety of birds, and the seeds are doubtless most commonly distributed through this agency. In addition to the fruits proper one may often find upon the branches the curious cedar-apples, a specimen of which is illustrated near the upper right-hand corner of the plate. These are due to the attacks of a parasitic fungus. The Red Cedar is often also called the Savin.

The approaching exhaustion of the supply of Cedar wood for lead pencils and other purposes has led to the recommendation that the species be more generally planted for forestry purposes. The fact, however that it grows very slowly, requiring seventy years to reach a good merchantable size renders such advice of little value to the average forest planter. Nursery grown trees are readily obtained for ornamental planting.

THE EUROPEAN YEW

M R. ALFRED REHDER has stated that the six species of Yew commonly recognized as growing in the northern hemisphere "are all very closely allied and could be considered geographical varieties of a single species." Of these the most notable is the European Yew, famous in English literature for many centuries and commonly grown in America as an ornamental tree. Like so many species that have been long in cultivation, many horticultural varieties have been developed. These variations have to do in some cases with the habit of growth, some being dwarf and shrublike, others tall and columnar; in other cases with the color of the foliage, some being yellow or golden, others whitish. One form has pendulous twigs.

In its normal condition the English Yew is a short-trunked tree with a top that sometimes reaches a height of sixty feet. It grows very slowly and many of the famous trees are of immemorial age. This slowness of growth doubtless is the cause of the extraordinary quality of the wood that formerly rendered it so valuable for making bows as well as in these later days for cabinet-making purposes. Many a hard-fought battle in the annals of old England has been decided through the use of

"The bows of double fatal yew."

The only species of Yew native to eastern North America is the American Yew (*Taxus Canadensis*) which is more commonly called the Ground Hemlock. This is a low shrub that never takes on the tree form, which is widely distributed throughout Canada and the Northern States, extending as far south as Virginia and Iowa. Its wood is of a yellowish brown color, very heavy, tough and elastic. The general appearance of the leafy branches is suggestive of those of the Hemlock, due to the flattened arrangement of the leaves which, however, are longer and more robust than those of the Hemlock. Each leaf is narrowed at the base into a short petiole and has a sharply-pointed tip. The midrib projects on both surfaces of the leaves, which are shining yellow green above and lighter below. The fruit is a curious red, berry-like object, formed by the disk becoming pulpy and cup-shaped so as almost to cover the hard seed. Small masses of the cut twigs have a curious musky odor, very different from that of any other of our evergreens. It is sometimes utilized in planting underwoods in large estates.

In a limited district in Northern Florida is a more or less tree-like Yew called the Florida Yew (*Taxus Floridana*) which is commonly ranked as a distinct species. On the Pacific coast is a more important form, often called the Oregon Yew (*Taxus brevifolia*), which extends from the Far North, south through California. The Indians utilize its wood for spears and bows while the bright berries serve probably as food for many birds.

EUROPEAN YEW

TAXUS BACCATA

GINKGO

GINKGO BILOBA

THE GINKGO TREE

WHEN one's attention is first called to the strangely curious leaves of the Ginkgo Tree or Maidenhair Tree one cannot but be struck with their extraordinary form and structure. They seem not at all like the leaves of a tree, and, to one who has examined under a reading glass the small leaflets of the Maidenhair Fern, these Ginkgo leaves will appear like magnified fern-leaves. The petiole is rather stout, somewhat grooved on the upper side, and it seems literally to expand into the fan-like blade of the leaf, nearly all of the veins arising from the enlarged end of the petiole and many of them giving off a few parallel branches which serve for the expansion of the leaf. The general form of the leaves, with their slight variations, is well shown on the plate. As will be seen, there is a deep cleft in the middle of the tip which sometimes extends nearly half way to the base.

It seems fitting that a tree with foliage so bizarre should have come from the Orient, and its name as well as its form easily suggests its Chinese origin. It is said to have been introduced into Japan from China and into England from Japan and into America from England. The foliage is of a very beautiful green color and this fact, together with its extraordinary form, has led it to be quite generally planted as an ornamental species in parks and private grounds. It grows slowly but there are now in America many trees which have been planted for thirty or forty years that have attained a large size, some of which bear small crops of the interesting fruit. The pollen-bearing and the seed-bearing flowers are borne in separate clusters, as may be seen in the upper right hand picture on the plate. The latter mature into curious plum-like drupes, the pulpy part of the fruit being ill-scented and valueless but the large inner nut having a good-sized kernel which after being roasted is much esteemed by the Orientals. These fruits, however, are proving an objectionable feature of the tree for street use in Washington, D. C., as they litter the sidewalks when they drop. This would not be so serious a matter on lawns and along fences, so that the latter situations are to be preferred in planting the trees.

The form of the older trees is well shown in the fine specimen illustrated on the plate. The general outline is suggestive of some of the Oaks, the wide-spreading branches giving a dense shade. The leaves turn yellow in autumn and fall off, although the Ginkgo Tree belongs to the great family of conifers, most of which retain their leaves through the winter. This tree is so beautiful and interesting that it deserves to be more generally planted in parks and private grounds.

THE CABBAGE PALMETTO

THE Palmetto or Cabbage Palmetto is one of the most characteristic features of the landscape in Florida and neighboring States. Although the species is found as far north as North Carolina, it does not attain there the size and dignity that it does along the gulf coast of Florida, where it becomes a large tree that adds a strange beauty to the borders of the lakes and rivers that abound in that region. The young trees are found everywhere in Florida, making a scrubby growth that the imagination of the Northern tourist is likely to people with rattlesnakes and other animals whose presence encourages him to keep to the main travelled roads.

The Palmetto is a typical example of the Palm family, the most notable of tree families in tropical regions. All the members of this group are characterized by growing straight upward from a single terminal bud, which in the case of this palmetto furnishes the so-called "cabbage," to which are due the names Cabbage Palmetto and Cabbage Tree, the large bud being commonly cooked and eaten, though its loss causes the death of the tree. All of the palms also have a curious rind-like bark, from which the thick, spreading leaf-stalks arise, stalks that remain upon the Palmetto tree long after the leaf-blades have broken off, giving the upper part of the trunk a curious and characteristic appearance.

The direct utility of the Palmetto is not confined to the furnishing of the sacrificial bud for cooking. The leaves serve admirably for the thatching of temporary roofs, and when young furnish strips which are used in the making of hats, baskets and similar articles. Parts of the leaf-stems and the outer bark are utilized in the manufacture of cheap scrubbing-brushes, while the trunks themselves, being durable under water and not attacked by the borers that affect wood in salt water, are quite generally used for wharf-piles.

In the Southeastern States the Palmetto makes an excellent tree for street and ornamental planting. Mr. H. Nehrling, who has made a special study of the growing of palms in Florida, writes in the "Cyclopedia of Horticulture:" "Even goodsized trees are not difficult to transplant if the whole stem is carefully dug out and all of the roots and leaves are cut off. If the stem has been set at least three feet deep, and the soil is kept well watered after planting, the Palmetto is almost sure to live." It responds quickly to good culture and an abundance of nitrogenous fertilizer.

Several other members of the Palm Family grow within the limits of the United States. The most splendid of these is the magnificent Royal Palm (*Roystonea regia*) which occurs in Southern Florida, as well as in the Bermudas, throughout the West Indies and in Central America. Other smaller palms occur along the Florida coast and adjacent islands, while in the far Southwest still other forms are found.

(58)

CABBAGE PALMETTO
SABAL PALMETTO

BUTTERNUT — WHITE WALNUT
JUGLANS CINEREA

THE BUTTERNUT

THE Butternut is one of the best known of all of the nut-bearing trees. It is distributed from New Brunswick to Delaware at sea level, and extends southward along the mountains to Georgia and Alabama. On the west it extends to Dakota, Nebraska, and Missouri, and is also found in Northeastern Arkansas.

The Butternut and the Black Walnut are at once distinguished from the Hickories at any season of the year by the presence in the twigs of a hollow, chambered pith. In winter the Butternut is distinguished from the Black Walnut by the dark brown pith and the transverse fringe of hairs that is found across the front border of the leaf-scar. The bark of the young twigs is of a deep yellow brown color, smooth and shining and dotted with many small, round, whitish spots. The buds are very characteristic, being covered with a dense yellowish brown pubescence, and forming with the curiously shaped leaf-scars a combination of characters that are easily remembered. The trees have a wide-spreading habit of branching which is very characteristic, especially in young specimens.

Early in May in the more northern regions the flowers of the Butternut appear just as the leaves are unfolding. The pollen-bearing and the seed-bearing blossoms are in separate groups upon the same tree, the former consisting of long catkins which generally project from the buds on the sides of the twigs near the ends. When they develop they are often six inches long and of a greenish color, becoming somewhat brownish as the florets mature. The seed-bearing flowers are much smaller, being borne either singly or in groups of a few blossoms and being green with rather strikingly colored red stigmas. Each floret consists of a small, hairy, four-lobed calyx with four small petals between the lobes. The tree depends upon the wind for the carrying of the pollen, and the flower has, as an adaptation to this method of pollination, an extraordinarily developed stigma. The long slender nuts are edible and are eagerly sought for every autumn.

The leaves of the Butternut bear a general resemblance to those of the Black Walnut. They are large compound leaves, and often reach an enormous size. When they first come out of the bud they are slightly pubescent, and are more or less covered with a sticky substance.

While the Butternut is often a very attractive tree as seen growing spontaneously, it is not to be depended upon for ornamental planting, as it is very apt to develop dead branches which interfere with its symmetry. Good-sized trees, even when growing under favorable conditions, generally show this disfigurement, and larger trees are very likely to die completely before they attain any great size. The species does not bear transplanting very well, and may best be reproduced by nuts planted where the trees are desired.

THE BLACK WALNUT

IN its best estate the Black Walnut is a magnificent tree. In open situations it attains a great size, in trunk as well as in spread of branches. Wherever it grows it is known by its very characteristic fruit, which is different from that of any other American tree, the large, hard-walled nuts being enclosed in a thick green husk that falls from the trees in October and which when bruised has a characteristic aromatic odor.

In winter the twigs of this species are easily distinguished from those of the Butternut by the absence of the fringe of hairs across the end of the leaf-scar, as well as by the light brown pith of the twigs. The bark of these twigs is slightly pubescent and generally of a brownish or grayish brown color. The leaf-scars are somewhat heart-shaped and the buds are covered with thick, dark brown, downy scales. The flowers appear in May when the leaves are unfolding, and closely resemble those of the Butternut. The compound leaves often attain a great length, the leaflets being sessile or nearly so and having their margins regularly serrate. The leaves have a distinctly aromatic odor when bruised.

The northern range of the Black Walnut extends from central New England west to Ontario and Minnesota, while its southern range extends from Florida west to Mississippi and Texas. Like so many other trees the species reaches its greatest development in the valley of the Ohio river, where specimens one hundred and fifty feet high and eight feet in diameter of trunk have frequently been found. It was these large trees that furnished the Black Walnut lumber which was formerly so highly prized in the manufacture of furniture and which is now very difficult to obtain.

As an ornamental tree the Black Walnut has the disadvantage that it comes into leaf rather late in spring and sheds its foliage somewhat early in autumn. It is best fitted for situations not too near buildings, where there is abundant room for it to develop and where the falling catkins, leaves, and nuts will not be objectionable. Aside from certain caterpillars which occasionally partially defoliate it, the tree has comparatively few enemies.

Two other native species of walnuts occur in the United States. The Southwestern Walnut (*Juglans rupestris*) is a spreading tree or shrub which occurs in Arizona, Texas, and New Mexico. It bears small nuts with thick shells and sweet kernels. The California Walnut (*Juglans Californica*) is a rather small tree or shrub which occurs along the coast of California. It also bears small nuts with sweet kernels, and shells thinner than those of the other species. The species is commonly used as a grafting stock for the English or Persian Walnut.

BLACK WALNUT
JUGLANS NIGRA

PECAN

HICORIA PECAN — CARYA OLIVÆFORMIS

WALNUT FAMILY

THE PECAN

THE Pecan is generally acknowledged to be the most important native nut-bearing tree in the United States. Throughout the region to which it is indigenous— the basin of the Mississippi as far north as Indiana, Illinois, and Iowa, as well as other Southern States—the value of the nuts for food has long been recognized, and during the last thirty years there has been a concerted attempt to improve the size and quality of the nuts and to establish commercial Pecan orchards. In such attempts many improved varieties have been introduced, and many methods of budding and grafting have been tried. Of course, a good proportion of such varieties have proved of little value for general culture, and many of the experiments in working over the trees have been failures. But from it all there has been substantial progress, and the value of the tree has been steadily gaining recognition. So marked is this improvement that the Southern experiment stations are publishing bulletins treating of the culture of the tree in a practical and scientific manner.

The relationship of the Pecan to our familiar hickory-nut is easily inferred from the pictures on the plate. The compound leaves with their slender, long-pointed decorative leaflets are very similar to the leaves of some of the Hickories; the long catkins of the pollen-bearing blossoms are substantially like those of the Hickories; and the nuts are essentially slender, thin-walled hickory-nuts. The trees often attain a height of one hundred and fifty feet and a trunk diameter of five or six feet. Such trees of course have been long in growing and are likely to be found only in the soil of rich river lands, like the famous region of the Wabash, where so many kinds of trees reach their largest size. The wood is brittle and of little value as compared with that of most of the other hickories. It is good for firewood, however.

On the supposition that a large percentage of the improved sorts would reproduce their type from seed, many thousands of seedlings were planted without budding or grafting. Experience soon showed that the nuts on the seedlings were not of the parent type, and the approved practice now is to bud or graft in the same way that varieties of apples and other fruits are maintained. There has been also a general top-working of established trees, a process in which success is difficult but well worth while, because many years of waiting are thus avoided.

Among the more important named varieties of the Pecan are Century, Frotscher, Pabst, Paragon, Sovereign, Stuart, and VanDeman.

THE BITTERNUT HICKORY OR SWAMP HICKORY

IN many respects the Bitternut is the most beautiful tree among the Hickories. It reaches a large size, with a comparatively smooth trunk that tapers very gradually from the bottom, with rather a wide spread of branches and a foliage which is remarkable for the smallness of the leaflets, a fact which gives to the tree in full foliage a more graceful appearance than that of the other Hickories. It is at once distinguished in summer by its pubescent petioles and leaflets which lack the aromatic fragrance that distinguishes the Mockernut. In autumn it may be known by the winged projections on the upper half of the fruit-husk, and in winter by the large orange-yellow buds which have none of the loose blackish outer scales that distinguish the Shagbark Hickory.

The small leaflets of the Bitternut are commonly ovate lanceolate in shape, and have distinctly serrate margins. The under surface, and sometimes to a slight extent the upper surface also, together with the midribs and the petioles, are hairy. Before falling in autumn the leaves change to a yellowish color.

In winter the bark of recent shoots is brown and rather smooth except for many slightly raised dots of a lighter color. The buds are of a characteristic orange-yellow color, generally somewhat hairy, those along the sides of the twigs being frequently four-angled, while those at the ends are considerable longer and often slightly curved. In spring the leaves appear, like those of the other Hickories rather late, and as they develop are commonly of a yellowish or reddish color, being thickly clothed with hairs. The blossoms develop in a manner similar to those of the related species.

The Bitternut seems by preference to be a lowland tree, although it is often found on uplands as well. It ranges from central New England west to Minnesota and south to Texas and Florida. In many parts of this vast territory it is a very abundant tree, being the commonest species of Hickory found in Iowa and neighboring states. It is often called the Swamp Hickory.

Another bitter-fruited Hickory is the Bitter Pecan or Water Hickory (*Hicoria aquatica*) which occurs in swampy regions of the Southern States. It is a slender tree of comparatively little value. The Nutmeg Hickory (*Hicoria myristicæformis*) is another southern species which is comparatively little known, but which is remarkable for the beauty of its shining leaves.

BITTERNUT HICKORY — SWAMP HICKORY
HICORIA MINIMA — CARYA AMARA

SHELLBARK HICKORY — SHAGBARK

HICORIA OVATA — CARYA ALBA

THE SHELLBARK OR SHAGBARK HICKORY

THE Shellbark Hickory is perhaps the most easily determined of the four species of Hickory that are commonly found in eastern America. At any season good-sized trees are known by the scaly bark of the trunk, which has given the species its common names of Shellbark and Shagbark Hickory. In summer it may also be known by the glabrous petioles and large leaves, the latter usually having five leaflets, of which the outer three are very broad. In autumn it may be identified by the fact that the husk of the fruit is nearly spherical and splits clear to the base along the four sutures. In winter it is easily distinguished by the loose, blackish outer scales on the buds, the bark of the twigs being smooth and not downy.

The fruit of the Shellbark Hickory is one of the favorite American nuts. Throughout the great regions in which it is found the gathering of these nuts is a recognized part of the autumn experiences of many boys, who sally forth with bags after the first frosts of October have sent the nuts to the ground. Nor is it the boys alone that find reward and nourishment in the fruit of these trees. The Hickory groves are the favorite resorts of the squirrels in October. James Russell Lowell pictured a familiar autumn sight when he wrote of the squirrel that—

> " on the shingly shagbark's bough
> Now saws, now lists with downward eye and ear,
> Then drops his nut."

The Shellbark Hickory is as famous for the quality of its wood as for its nuts. On account of its toughness, lightness, and elasticity, it has long been a favorite material for axe-handles and other implements in which these qualities are required. Unfortunately the supply of trees for lumber purposes has been greatly diminished, and many other woods which are less desirable are now being utilized in place of the Hickory. Large trees reach a height of more than a hundred feet and a trunk diameter of three or four feet, but generally the trees are only about two-thirds this size. When grown in the forest the trunk is notable for clear length without branches, it frequently being fifty feet from the ground to the lowest branch.

The natural range of the Shagbark extends on the north from Maine to Michigan and Minnesota and on the south from Florida to Texas. Along the eastern seaboard it is found chiefly in the mountains in the region south of Delaware. On account of its long tap-root the Hickory is proverbially difficult to transplant. When once established it grows rather rapidly and has many claims for a place in landscape planting, although it is not one of the trees which is most desirable on small grounds.

THE MOCKERNUT OR BIG BUD HICKORY

IN summer the easiest way to determine the Mockernut Hickory is to see that the petioles of the leaves are pubescent and that the blades have a strong aromatic fragrance, especially when slightly bruised. The lower surface of the blade is usually more or less pubescent, and there are generally five or seven leaflets. In autumn the species is to be distinguished by the fact that the fruit husk has strongly indented sutures, and also by the downy bark on the young twigs. The nuts vary greatly in size, but generally they are very large, and have thick shells which are commonly four-angled on account of prominent vertical ridges on the outside. The kernel of the nut is sweet and edible, but does not fill the cavities so completely as does the kernel of the Shagbark. It is commonly supposed that this smallness of the kernel, as compared with the size of the nut outwardly, gave to the species its common name.

Like the other Hickories the flowers of the Mockernut develop in spring as the leaves are nearing full size. The pollen-bearing blossoms are in slender catkins arranged in groups that arise from the base of the new season's shoots. They are green, and hang downward for several inches. The seed-bearing flowers are generally in groups of two or more at the ends of the new branches. Pollination is brought about by the wind.

In the more northern parts of its range the Mockernut seems by preference to be a hillside tree, being found most abundantly on rocky hills and mountain slopes. Its northern range extends from central New England west to Ontario, and its southern from Florida west to Kansas and Texas. Full-grown trees reach a height of seventy or even a hundred feet and a trunk diameter of three feet, such large specimens more commonly occurring in the South than in the North. Professor Sargent writes that this is "the only Hickory in the southern maritime Pine-belt, growing in great abundance on low sandy hummocks close to the shores of bays and estuaries along the coast of the South Atlantic and Gulf States." It is often called the Big Bud Hickory, and its wood has much the same value and is used for the same purposes as that of the Shagbark Hickory.

As in the case of many other trees various forms of hickories are often found which have characters intermediate between well-known species. Such trees are supposed to be natural hybrids. Trees which indicate such hybridizing between the Mockernut and the Pecan are occasionally seen, as well as others that indicate hybridizing between the Mockernut and other hickories.

MOCKERNUT -- BIG BUD HICKORY
HICORIA ALBA — CARYA TOMENTOSA

PIGNUT HICKORY
HICORIA GLABRA — CARYA PORCINA

THE PIGNUT HICKORY

THE Pignut Hickory is most easily distinguished in summer by the glabrous petioles and the small leaflets, the latter being smooth and generally five to seven on each leaf. In autumn it is distinguished by the fact that the fruit-husk does not split to the base, as well as by its small yellowish-brown buds. The quality of the kernel of the nut varies greatly, commonly being bitter but sometimes having a sweetish taste. The nut is rather small, with a thick or thin shell that is usually more or less four-angled toward the tip.

For a Hickory the outline of the Pignut tree in winter is graceful and attractive. This is largely due to the fact that the twigs are unusually slender, so that their tracery against the sky as seen at a little distance seems composed of delicate lines. The bark of the young shoots is of a reddish-brown or brownish-red color, marked with linear whitish spots. The bark of the trunk is dark gray in color, and is rather smooth, not being so closely and distinctly furrowed as is that of the Mockernut, nor peeling off in great scales as does that of the Shellbark Hickory.

The flowers of the Pignut develop rather late in spring, about the time the leaves are nearly full grown, and resemble in their general structure those of the other Hickories. The yellowish anthers are partially clothed with whitish hairs. The fully-developed leaves have the blades yellowish green on the upper surface and paler on the under surface. In autumn they change to a yellowish or an orange brown before falling.

The Pignut is essentially a tree of upland rather than lowland habitat. It has a wide range, extending from Maine and Ontario west to Michigan and Nebraska, and south to Texas and Florida. Like so many other trees, it reaches its largest size in the Ohio Valley, where trees one hundred and twenty feet high with a trunk diameter of five feet are sometimes found. Generally, however, in other parts of its range the tree is much smaller when it attains its full size. Young trees may be raised from the nuts, and a few add variety and interest to any place of pretentious size.

Eleven species of hickories are commonly recognized in America, North of Mexico. Aside from those already discussed the Big Shellbark or Bottom Shellbark (*Hicoria laciniosa*) is one of the most important. It is a tall tree rather common in the Central West, which bears large nuts that are commonly sold in the markets of many cities.

THE ASPEN

THE trembling aspen leaf has been referred to in literature perhaps as often as any other phase of tree life. Poets in all ages have utilized it as a simile that has appealed to the consciousness of everyone. In the Odyssey we read:

> " Some wove the web,
> Or twirled the spindle, sitting, with a quick
> Light motion like the aspen's glancing leaves."

In the later poets references to this leaf are legion. One of the most familiar is the line in that charming verse of Lowell's,—

> " Only the pattering aspen
> Made a sound of growing rain,
> That fell faster and faster,
> Then faltered to silence again."

The structural peculiarity which gives so distinctive a character to this most abundant of the Poplars is well worth a moment's examination. The rather thin leaf has a comparatively broad blade, set at right angles to the long, slender, greatly flattened petiole. At its base this petiole is firmly attached to the twig by means of a clasping enlargement. As the leaves hang downward on these slender stems the slightest breath of wind changes the position of the blades, twisting the petioles in so doing, and the elasticity of the latter is continually bringing the blades back into their original position. Thus we have the trembling foliage which is the most distinctive character of the tree.

This Aspen is distinguished from the Large-toothed Aspen and the Cottonwood by the finely serrate margins of the leaves. In winter and early spring it is distinguished from the former by its smooth, varnish-like buds, and from the latter by its comparatively small buds, which seldom exceed half an inch in length. These buds develop in earliest spring into long, slender catkins, those on some trees being pollen-bearing and on other trees seed-bearing. The pollen is cast to the winds in great abundance and wafted from tree to tree. The seeds develop late in May or early in June, and are covered with a cottony down by means of which they ride long distances on the wings of the wind.

This is the species most likely to spring up in clearings which have been burned over. In such a poplar grove the trees are gracefully symmetrical, with smooth, pale green bark which is marked with darker blotches below the junction of the branches. The coloring of this bark varies greatly with the weather conditions. After a period of rain it becomes of an olive green, which is one of the most beautiful colors to be found in nature. Artists have long delighted to paint the trunk of the Birch, but few of them apparently have ever attempted to put on canvas this wonderful color of the Poplar trunk during the long weeks of early spring.

ASPEN
POPULUS TREMULOIDES

LARGE-TOOTHED ASPEN — POPLAR

POPULUS GRANDIDENTATA

THE LARGE-TOOTHED ASPEN OR POPLAR

DURING a brief period in early spring the Large-toothed Poplar is the most conspicuous tree in the forest. When the buds are pushing into leaves the young growth is so thickly covered with a cottony down that the white tree stands forth strongly revealed against the darker background of the neighboring branches. When the leaves are fully expanded much of this whiteness is lost and the tree resumes its normally inconspicuous position among its neighbors.

Some time before the developing leaves show themselves the tree sends out its long, pendent festoons of greenish gray, or reddish, odorless blossoms, those bearing pollen upon one tree being reddish while those bearing pistils upon another, are gray green, the species depending upon the wind to carry the fertilizing pollen from the one to the other. In appearance these blossoming catkins resemble those of the Aspen, but a close examination will show a hairy covering upon the scales at the base of the catkins instead of the varnish-like coating upon the bud-scales of the Aspen. The seeds mature in May or June, and are covered with a wooly down that enables them to float in the air.

In summer the Large-toothed Aspen is easily distinguished by its good-sized leaves, coarsely dentate on the margins, with long, vertically flattened petioles that give the blades great freedom of motion. The side margins of the blades are usually turned upward so that the upper surface of the leaf is concave, a circumstance which renders them much more likely to be constantly twisted by the wind than if the blades were flat. In autumn the leaves turn yellow before falling, some of those on the tips of the twigs occasionally assuming a beautiful orange-red hue. The leaves on the suckers that spring up from underground roots or about the base of a stump are very different from the normal leaves of the species, being larger, generally serrate rather than dentate, and commonly covered on the under surface with a cottony down.

The bark of the tree-trunk is usually dark gray in color and marked with rather short vertical furrows which, on trees of medium size, do not extend very far. The bark, as a rule, is distinctly darker than the bark of Aspen trees of corresponding size, and there is not so striking a difference in color at the junction of the branches with the trunk as there is in the case of the Aspen. The buds are pointed and downy, the latter being a distinguishing characteristic.

This species is native to a great region in the Northeast, extending from Nova Scotia, Quebec and Minnesota on the north to Iowa, Kentucky and Delaware on the South.

THE BALSAM POPLAR OR TACAMAHAC

TO see this magnificent tree at its best one should visit some of the great streams of British America, where it grows to a height of a hundred feet and is a most conspicuous feature in the forest landscape. It extends from the Atlantic to the Pacific coast, and continues south as far as Maine in the East and as Nebraska and Nevada in the West, extending north to Labrador and Alaska. In Sir John Franklin's report of his last journey, he wrote that "the greatest part of the drift timber we observed on the shores of the Arctic Sea was Balsam Poplar."

When one unfamiliar with this tree first sees it growing isolated upon a hillside in Northern New England, the tree seems especially remarkable for its straight, erect trunk, and its slender, symmetrical outline. The leaves in the typical form are ovate lanceolate, being much narrower than those of the familiar Balm of Gilead. The upper surface is dark green and the under surface much paler. It has a characteristic balsamic odor by which it may always be distinguished. The winter buds are much like those of the Cottonwood and the Balm of Gilead, being large, long, slender, and acutely pointed. The flower-buds are much larger than the leaf-buds, the former developing in early spring into the characteristic catkins illustrated in the upper right-hand corner of the plate, where the seed-bearing blossoms are next the right margin and the pollen-bearing at the left. After being fertilized by the pollen the former elongate into the fruiting catkins, one of which is shown in the lower illustration on the left of the plate.

Like all of the Willows and Poplars, this species may easily be multiplied by means of branches cut off and set in moist soil. In a short time they will send out roots through the bark, and rapidly develop a root-system that enables them to start their growth anew. Any of these trees form excellent objects to utilize for planting in school gardening work. If each child were encouraged to start such a little tree at school, and when it had developed a root-system encouraged to take it home and plant it in some desirable situation, a great impetus might readily be given to the movement for tree-planting. The tree garden is likely to become indeed one of the important phases of nature study in the schools, as it furnishes admirable opportunities for the pupils to become acquainted with the trees as well as to acquire a practical knowledge of some of the most interesting horticultural operations.

BALSAM POPLAR — TACAMAHAC

POPULUS BALSAMIFERA

BALM OF GILEAD

POPULUS BALSAMIFERA CANDICANS

THE BALM OF GILEAD

THE broad-leaved Balm of Gilead has been very extensively planted as a shade tree throughout the Eastern States. Its origin, as well as its precise botanical standing, seems to be a matter of great uncertainty. It is generally considered a variety of the widely distributed Balsam Poplar, or Tacamahac, but some authorities give it rank as a distinct species. It is easily known by its large, shiny leaves, which are more nearly heart-shaped than those of almost any other tree, and which have a distinct balsamic odor. The petioles are rather stout, flattened vertically, and generally somewhat pubescent, especially toward the base. The margins are regularly crenately serrate and under a lens may be seen to have a sparse pubescence. The apex is generally acuminate, sometimes simply acute. The under surface of the leaf is lighter green than the upper surface. In autumn the blades change to a distinct yellow, while the petioles become either yellow or reddish.

In winter the Balm of Gilead may be readily known by the large buds upon the twigs, these buds having a strong balsamic odor and a distinct coating of balsam between the scales. The bark of the twigs is generally of an olive-brown color with a shining surface. The trees often reach a height of fifty or sixty feet, with the bark of the upper part of the trunk rather smooth and of a greenish-gray color while that of the lower part of the trunk is likely to be ridged and much darker. In spring the blossoms appear slightly later than those of the common Aspen, the catkins being long and slender and grayish or greenish in color. Curiously enough, no one seems to have been able to find any pollen-bearing catkins on the trees of this variety, all of those present being the seed-bearing forms. But these commonly do not set seed because of the lack of pollen and soon drop off, lying under the trees in a way to suggest an army of hairy caterpillars. The young leaves are thickly covered with resinous hairs. These are especially abundant on the petioles and the margins of the blades.

As a shade tree the Balm of Gilead has both advantages and disadvantages. It is easily propagated from cuttings or suckers and it grows rapidly. It furnishes a rather dense shade, and its general effect is pleasing. Its roots extend deep into the ground, so that it is able to forage far beneath the pavements of city streets. Its leaves are smooth and shining, and not easily clogged by the dust and smoke of city chimneys. On the other hand, the odor of the twigs is disagreeable to some people, the falling catkins and leaves are sometimes troublesome, and the tendency to send up shoots or suckers from the roots is often a serious objection.

THE COTTONWOOD

DURING recent years the Cottonwood has been very largely utilized for ornamental planting in the streets, parks and private grounds of many of our cities. For such purposes it has the advantage of ease of propagation by means of cuttings which enable the nurserymen to offer the trees at a low price, of rapidity of growth, giving a considerable shade a very few years after planting, of comparative freedom from insect or fungus attack, and of smoothness of foliage which keeps clean even in the smoke-laden atmosphere of the manufacturing cities, where large quantities of soft coal are used. A variety most commonly sold is the Carolina Poplar, and probably in many cities the species is better known by that name than by the name of Cottonwood.

In summer this species is most easily distinguished by means of the broad leaves with the rounded, forward-pointing teeth along the margins, these teeth commonly extending in a more or less modified form clear around to the junction of the petiole with the blade. The base is generally cut more or less squarely off and is not heart-shaped, a fact which distinguishes it at once from the leaf of the Balm of Gilead. The apex is long, slender and sharply pointed. These leaves more nearly resemble those of the Lombardy Poplar than any of the other species, but they are generally to be distinguished from the latter by the fact that they are longer in proportion to their breadth than are the leaves of the Lombardy Poplar, while the tree of course is to be distinguished by its more horizontal direction of the larger limbs. Both surfaces of the leaf are smooth, shining green, the upper side being somewhat darker than the under side. In Winter the Cottonwood is notable for its very large buds which resemble in a general way those of the Balm of Gilead but lack the strong distinctive odor of the latter species. The young shoots are greenish or greenish brown, often more or less striped with longitudinal lines or spotted with grayish dots. The twigs of large trees which have borne blossoming catkins are commonly marked by the swollen bases to which these catkins were attached, giving the branch a curiously irregular appearance.

The Cottonwood is indigenous to a great region extending from Vermont and Quebec on the north and from the Rocky Mountains on the west to New Mexico, Pennsylvania, Maryland and Florida on the south. In the more eastern parts of its range it is neither so large nor so abundant as in the Central West, where it becomes one of the most characteristic trees. It has been very largely used for planting in the Great Plains region, forming probably the commonest tree upon which tree claims for land were based. In the Middle West **vast numbers of** natural seedlings grow every year upon the sandy bars and shores of the rivers. These are readily transplanted to other situations. The species is even more easily reproduced by cuttings of vigorous twigs half an inch in diameter and about two feet long.

COTTONWOOD
POPULUS DELTOIDEA

SALICACEÆ

LOMBARDY POPLAR
POPULUS NIGRA ITALICA

WILLOW AND POPLAR FAMILY

THE LOMBARDY POPLAR

THE Lombardy Poplar is one of the most interesting trees cultivated by man. It was formerly believed to have originated in Lombardy many hundreds of years ago in some specimen that assumed the peculiar manner of growth that characterizes the tree, but during recent years the species is said to have been found growing wild in Afghanistan, high up in the mountains. It is an interesting fact that all of the Lombardy Poplar trees which have been grown by man have borne only pollen-bearing blossoms, so that the species has been reproduced by cuttings or suckers exclusively, no seed being possible under existing conditions. If the species does grow wild in its native home it ought to be possible to introduce seed-bearing trees.

The vertical habit of growth of the branches of the Lombardy Poplar at once distinguishes the tree from all others. The leaf also is characteristic, being very broad for its length. The base is usually truncate or wedge-shaped and the apex is acutely pointed, while the margin of the blade is finely crenulate or serrate. The buds are small and vertically pointed, the flower-buds developing very early in spring into pollen-bearing catkins, and the leaf-buds pushing out a little later their young leaves of a rich yellow-green color. The petioles are appressed but rather strong, holding the leaves firmly in their general position but allowing them to move freely from side to side in the wind. In consequence the blades are constantly shifting in unison, the observation of which fact led Leigh Hunt to write—

" The poplar shoot
Which like a feather waves from head to foot."

There has been much discussion concerning the place of the Lombardy Poplar in landscape gardening. In former times it was planted everywhere as an ornamental tree. Somewhat later it suffered from a reaction which led to its general neglect. At present the fact seems to be recognized that a tree with so distinctive a character may be of inestimable value in some parts of a landscape picture while in other parts it may be worse than useless. One situation in which I have lately seen it used to great advantage is in a little park where a group of trees surround a tall flag-pole. There are many such poles which could be helped by such planting. It is easily propagated by cuttings of the branches and grows very rapidly.

THE WHITE POPLAR

FEW trees have been so often referred to in European literature as the White Poplar. It has been associated with men more intimately than almost any other species, and has been the subject of numerous legends and traditions in the folk-lore of many peoples. In America it was planted about the homes of the earliest colonists, and has often spread quite widely from these originally imported trees.

The most striking feature of the White Poplar is found in the differing color of the two surfaces of the leaves. The upper side is a very dark green, which in shadow is almost black, while the under surface is of a glistening white that shows in a very striking manner when the wind blows violently. Cowper wrote of

" The poplar that with silver lines his leaf,"

and Tennyson mentions

" Blasts that blow the poplar white,"

while our own Aldrich has said,

" We knew it would rain for the poplars showed
The white of their leaves."

This silvery pubescence is not by any means confined to the leaves. In winter the White Poplar is at once distinguished from all the other species by the dense, cottony down that covers the buds and twigs. The tree often attains a large size, and the grayish bark of the trunk is generally rough aud irregular.

Like the other Poplars the pollen-bearing and seed-bearing flowers are upon separate trees. The flower-buds are large and conspicuous and develop very early in spring into long, drooping catkins. The cottony seeds mature a few weeks later and are scattered far and wide by the wind. Thickets of young poplars commonly grow up around neglected trees, arising from underground shoots that spread in all directions. The leaves on such vigorous young trees are thickly covered with cottony down giving to the thicket a very white appearance that is sure to attract attention.

WHITE POPLAR

POPULUS ALBA

BLACK WILLOW
SALIX NIGRA

THE BLACK WILLOW

THE Black Willow is distributed over practically the entire eastern region of North America, extending from New Brunswick to Florida and from the Atlantic coast to Nebraska, Kansas, Texas, and even into parts of California. It attains its largest size in the Mississippi Valley, where it is the most abundant of the tree-like Willows, sometimes reaching a height of more than a hundred feet and a trunk diameter of two or three feet. As in the case of the other Willows, it is especially likely to be found along the banks of streams or the margins of ponds and lakes. It is generally to be distinguished by its long, slender, narrowly-pointed leaves with their finely serrate margins, and the shining yellow-green color of both surfaces of the blades, the under surface being somewhat paler than the upper. Frequently the leaf is bent in a slightly sickle fashion. At the base of the rather short petiole there is a pair of rounded stipules that clasp the twig. These stipules are very characteristic, and are well shown in the accompanying plate.

The Black Willow blossoms rather late in spring but before the leaves have reached their full size, the latter appearing later than the leaves of the other Willows. The pollen-bearing and the seed-bearing catkins are upon separate trees, the former being shown on the extreme left of the pictures in the plate while the latter are shown in the adjoining illustration. The plant depends upon bees and other insects to carry the pollen from one kind of catkin to the other, secreting for this purpose an abundant supply of nectar and advertising it by the distinctive odor as well as by the rather conspicuous colors of the pollen-bearing catkins. In a very few weeks the cottony seeds are shed by the small capsules and are scattered far and wide by wind and water. According to the fine observation of Thoreau many of the latter "drift and form a thick white scum together with other matter, especially against some Alder or other fallen or drooping shrub where there is less current than usual. There within two or three days a great many germinate and show their two little roundish leaves, more or less tingeing with green the surface of the scum, somewhat like grass-seed in a tumbler of cotton. Many of these are drifted in among the button bushes, willows and other shrubs and the sedge along the river side, and the water falling just at this time when they have put forth little fibres they are deposited on the mud just left bare in the shade, and thus probably a great many of them have a chance to become perfect plants." Like the other willows this species probably reproduces even more frequently from twigs lodged along the banks of streams.

THE GLAUCOUS WILLOW

FOR a brief period in early spring the Glaucous Willow adds the final touch of beauty to the landscape. It dots the hillsides and the water-courses with the yellow tones of its pollen-bearing blossoms and the delicate greens of its seed-bearing catkins, making for a week or two the greatest show of any of the trees or shrubs. The blossoming branches attract the visits of a host of small bees, which come out of their winter burrows very early in the spring and gather from the pussy willows nectar and pollen to provision their nests. The flowers are also sought out by the queen bumblebees, the early butter-flies, and certain other insects which serve the plant by carrying pollen from one kind of flower to the other, and thus enable it to develop the small fruits which, late in spring or early in summer, break open and allow the downy seeds to be wafted away by the wind.

The Glaucous Willow is more likely to be found as a shrub than as a tree, although in Northern New England it very commonly assumes the tree form, some of the trees reaching a diameter of ten or twelve inches. The species ranges from Nova Scotia to Manitoba on the north, extending southward to Missouri, Illinois, and North Carolina. In summer it may usually be distinguished by the whitish color of the under leaf-surface, the leaves having slightly and sparsely serrate margins, and the general form shown in the right-hand picture of the plate.

This is preëminently the Pussy Willow, being the species to which this title is properly applied. It is very easily reproduced from cuttings and is of decided value in landscape planting, especially along water courses, where its roots serve to hold the banks of the stream in place, and where also its flowers in early spring add their unique beauty to the landscape.

As is well known the willows are the despair of the botanists. Nearly two hundred species have been described, and there appear to be besides innumerable natural hybrids that render exact classification, even to the specialist, almost impossible. Consequently the lay reader may well be content to identify a very few of the most distinctive kinds. He can if he so desires start a willow garden through cuttings and thus be able to follow each sort through the year.

GLAUCOUS WILLOW — PUSSY WILLOW
SALIX DISCOLOR

WHITE WILLOW

SALIX ALBA

WILLOW AND POPLAR FAMILY

THE WHITE WILLOW

A FEW weeks after the Pussy Willow has held the centre of the stage in the play of the changing seasons, the White Willow assumes the chief rôle. Throughout the great range in which this species is abundant one can scarcely look in any direction without seeing the landscape lighted up in a most wonderful fashion by the yellow bloom of these beautiful trees. In the hill regions especially one can see them marking the water-courses for a long distance, in a way which is the despair of any human decorator. In most parts of the country the more brilliantly colored pollen-bearing trees have been planted by Nature or by man almost exclusively, so that the less conspicuous blossoms of the seed-bearing forms are only rarely found. The catkins develop on the ends of the young branches which bear also the partially-developed leaves. This results in the yellow flowers being shown against a background of tender green foliage, which renders them conspicuous for long distances and attracts the visits of hosts of bees and other flying insects.

The White Willow is the largest of our common Willows, and very generally several trees are found growing together in the characteristic fashion shown in the lower picture on the plate. The branches for the most part project upward, and the bark of the trunk of large trees is roughened by numerous coarse ridges and is of a dark-gray color. There are a number of varieties of this species, the coloring of the twigs and leaves varying somewhat according to the variety. As the young leaves develop they are generally sparsely clothed with silken hairs on both surfaces, many of these hairs remaining upon the under surface

The species is supposed to be a native of Europe, apparently having been introduced into America very early in its modern history. It is easily propagated from cuttings and is of great value for ornamental planting. The tree most commonly seen is the Golden Osier Willow known technically as *Salix alba* variety *vitellina*. It is especially notable for the golden yellow of its twigs, rendering it a beautiful plant for winter hedge-row effects.

Very few introduced trees have become so thoroughly naturalized as has the White Willow. The ability of the broken twigs to take root along the water courses is doubtless an important reason for this result.

THE WEEPING WILLOW

VERY few of the trees which we see about us to-day can be traced back to the time and the country of the Psalmist. The Weeping or Babylon Willow is one of these: to it the poet who wrote the One Hundred and Thirty-Seventh Psalm referred in the familiar lines: "By the waters of Babylon we sat down and wept, when we remembered thee, O Zion! As for our harps we hanged them up upon the willow trees that are therein."

From that early time to this the Babylon Willow seems to have been a favorite tree in the Orient. It is widely distributed in Asia, and in China it is one of the most universally planted of all trees. It is supposed to have been first introduced into Europe about 1702 by the botanist and traveller Tournefort, who returned from a trip to the Levant in that year, but has probably been introduced independently at various times. One such case is attested by the anecdote concerning Pope, according to which the poet planted a willow withe which bound a package received from Turkey by Lady Suffolk. The twig grew into a famous tree in Twickenham garden, which attracted so many visitors that it was finally cut down by a later owner of the estate. In the Eighteenth and Nineteenth Centuries the Weeping Willow became very popular in Europe and it was generally planted for ornament early in our American history.

This tree is often called Napoleon's Willow, because of the association of the great commander with it during his exile. In life he sat under its shade and after death at least one tree grew about his island grave. From this tree many cuttings have been taken to be planted in other regions.

As one would expect from a tree so long in cultivation, there are many horticultural varieties of the Babylon Willow. One of the best of these is the Golden-barked Babylonian Willow, the yellow branches showing a glowing yellow in winter which makes them very attractive. Another variety is from France and is named Salamonii: it is said to make a more vigorous upright growth than the type, although the twigs retain the pendent habit.

The distinctive characteristics of the Babylon Willow are shown upon the plate. as will be seen the stems, leaves, and blossom-catkins are slender and delicate, while the tree itself, as seen in the picture of a fine specimen in the Boston Public Gardens, is of upright habit with the long terminal twigs drooping in graceful curves. It is a pity that the idea of grief should be so associated with this splendid tree. "Its expression," writes a keen and symphathetic observer of trees, Mr. J. Horace McFarland, "is rather of great dignity, and I remember watching in somewhat of awe one which grew near my childhood's home, as its branches writhed and twisted in a violent rainstorm, seeming then fairly to agonize, so tossed and buffeted were they by the wind. But soon the storm ceased, the sun shone on the rounded head of the willow, turning the raindrops to quickly vanishing diamonds, and the great tree breathed only a gentle and benignant peace."

HORNBEAM — BLUE BEECH
CARPINUS CAROLINIANA

THE HORNBEAM OR BLUE BEECH

THIS tree owes its name of Hornbeam to the exceeding hardness of the wood, which led the early settlers to call it "the Horne-bound tree." It owes its other common name, Blue Beech, to the striking resemblance between the bark of the young trees and that of the beech, it having, however, a slightly bluish color which furnishes the defining adjective. In summer the leaves bear a general resemblance to those of the Hop Hornbeam, being slightly thicker in texture and more slender in form. In early autumn, however, the difference between the foliage of the two trees is very striking. While the leaves of the Hop Hornbeam change to a clear yellow color those of the Hornbeam change to a brilliant orange-red or deep crimson.

Throughout the summer and autumn the curious fruits are likely to be found upon the trees and serve at once to identify it. As will be seen by reference to the picture, these consist of small nut-like objects clustered at the base of long triangular bracts that form a distinctive involucre.

The Blue Beech blossoms in April or May, the pollen-bearing and the seed-bearing flowers being produced in different catkins upon the same tree. The pollen-bearing catkins are borne along the sides of the branches rather than at the tip, as is the case with the Hop Hornbeam. During the winter they are enclosed in large buds two or three times the size of the leaf-buds. In habit of growth the tree is low and spreading, seldom attaining a diameter of more than a foot or a height of more than thirty feet. On most trees there are projecting ridges running vertically along the trunk which give it a characteristic appearance. The tree is likely to be found in damp places and in low woods, especially along the margins of swamps or slow-running streams. On account of the interesting character of the trunk and branches, and the beautiful coloring of the autumn foliage, it may be planted to advantage for landscape effects throughout its range, which covers practically the entire eastern region of North America. It is propagated from seed, and is especially likely to flourish where there is abundance of moisture.

The European Hornbeam (*Carpinus Betulus*) is an equally interesting tree. The wood has been utilized for many centuries for making ox-yokes and other domestic articles, while the living trees have been planted for hedges, arbors, and various formal garden purposes. This species seems also to grow naturally in the shade of taller trees and in damp situations.

THE HOP HORNBEAM OR IRONWOOD

AMONG all the leaves of the forest it would be difficult to find one of more exquisitely beautiful texture than that of the Hop Hornbeam. The blade is thin and translucent, showing a delicate tracery of veins and veinlets. The margin is doubly, yet finely, serrate, and the general outline is a beautiful, irregular oval, carried upward to an acuminate tip. The petiole is very short and the base of the leaf is slightly heart-shaped. These leaves are held on long, slender, interlacing branches which give the tree a distinctive character. Through most of the year these branches are tipped with pairs or trios of slender, cylindrical catkin-buds, which develop early in spring into long, pendent pollen-bearing catkins that yield the pollen which fertilizes the seed-bearing catkins, sent out along the sides of the twigs at the same period. As the months go by the latter mature into curious, hop-like fruits that give to this Hornbeam its definitive adjective.

In October the leaves gradually turn to a beautiful yellow color and drop lightly to the ground, revealing a tree which is easily recognized throughout the winter by the extraordinary slenderness of its interlacing twigs and the characteristic bark of the trunk and larger branches. The bark is thickly furrowed with narrow vertical grooves, the bark between the grooves being in short, narrow scales, each scale usually raised at the ends but tightly fastened in the middle. The hardness of the wood has been proverbial for hundreds of years and has led the tree to be called Ironwood perhaps more commonly than by any other name. The wood is especially useful in the manufacture of tools where great strength is required.

The Hop Hornbeam is commonly a tree of the underwoods. It occurs very far north in Canada, south to Florida and Texas, and reaches its greatest development in the Southwestern States, where the trees sometimes attain a height of fifty or sixty feet, although commonly they are only half this height.

A closely related tree called the Western Ironwood (*Ostrya Knowltoni*) occurs in Arizona although so far as now known but in one locality. It reaches a height of thirty feet and a trunk diameter of eighteen inches.

HOP HORNBEAM — IRONWOOD

OSTRYA VIRGINIANA

BLACK BIRCH — CHERRY BIRCH
BETULA   LENTA

THE BLACK BIRCH OR CHERRY BIRCH

THE popular names of this species are more fortunate than in the case of most trees having more than one such appellation. It is the Black Birch because the bark of the trunk is very dark, much more distinctly black than that of any of the other birches. It is the Sweet Birch because the tender bark of the young twigs has a pleasing and aromatic taste, which has led it to become well known to every country dweller throughout its range. It is the Cherry Birch because of the general resemblance of the tree to the Cherry.

In addition to the black, comparatively smooth bark of the trunk this tree may be known by the finely serrate, heart-shaped leaves which commonly appear on the ends of short twigs in groups of two or three. The pollen-bearing catkins develop early in the spring, having extraordinary length and producing a vast quantity of greenish-yellow pollen which is scattered far and wide by the wind, some of it falling upon the florets of the erect, seed-bearing catkins projecting along the sides of the branches of the same or other trees. The latter develop late in the season into erect, broad, fruiting catkins, which are generally shorter than those of the Canoe Birch. The trees commonly attain a large size and occur in a great variety of situations. They seem to thrive best on damp hillsides, or in other places where there is a moderate amount of moisture. The species is widely distributed from Nova Scotia to Minnesota, south to Kansas and Delaware, and extends along the mountains through the Southern States.

It was given its technical name, *Betula lenta*, by the great Linnæus. It is a useful tree for planting in parks and on home grounds, developing in the open a wide, symmetrical head which is very attractive.

In the far West there is a tree sometimes called the Western Black Birch (*Betula fontinalis*) which occurs in the mountain cañons. It is not a tall species, seldom if ever exceeding forty feet in height.

THE YELLOW BIRCH

OVER a large part of northern New England the Yellow Birch is one of the most abundant trees of the hardwood forests. It is easily recognized wherever it grows by its rather ragged yellowish or yellow-gray bark. The precise tint varies greatly in different trees, but it always differs from the bark of any of the other birches. On account of its abundance as a forest tree it is very largely used for fuel, lumber, and paper pulp.

The leaves of the Yellow Birch are quite similar to those of the Black Birch, the bases being cordate and the margins finely serrate; but the bark of the twigs has only to a slight degree the characteristic aromatic flavor of the Black Birch. In spring the long, pollen-bearing catkins which are pushed out from the ends of the branches are very similar in the two species, though the fruits which mature in autumn are more ovoid in the Black Birch and more cylindrical in the Yellow Birch.

The Yellow Birch is essentially a Northern tree, reaching its largest size in Canada and the Northeastern States, where it often attains a height of a hundred feet and a trunk diameter of four feet. In a forest the outline of the tree is generally modified by the presence of the surrounding trees, but in open spots the branches spread widely and are often somewhat pendulous, so that the tree is likely to take on a broadly rounded outline. The species occurs naturally from Newfoundland to Delaware, following the Alleghany Mountains southward to Tennessee. It extends west to Minnesota. In the more southern parts of its range it seldom attains a large size.

As an ornamental tree the variable yellowish bark is one of the most attractive features of the Yellow Birch. It was apparently this beauty of the tree that led Thoreau to visit so often what he called the "Yellow Birch Swamp." Young trees may be transplanted successfully, and flourish best in a damp situation where the roots can always reach sufficient moisture. The tree is hardy and little subject to attack by insect or fungus enemies.

The loose bark is very useful to hunters and campers in starting fires and the tree is always a favorite with lovers of the great north woods.

YELLOW BIRCH
BETULA LUTEA

RED OR RIVER BIRCH
BETULA NIGRA

THE RED BIRCH OR RIVER BIRCH

THE Red Birch is more happily called the River Birch, for of all the trees that haunt the borders of rivers this is perhaps the most constant. It is an attractive and picturesque tree as it grows singly or in small groups along the banks of a good-sized river, its dark foliage and ragged red bark forming a pleasing spectacle against the glistening water. It is comparatively a Southern species, rarely being found as far north as Canada although extremely abundant along the banks of the Merrimack river in Southern New Hampshire and Massachusetts, and extending southward along the Atlantic coast to Florida and westward along the Gulf to Texas. It attains its largest size in these southern regions, where no other kind of Birch is found.

The River Birch is readily identified by the hairiness of the smaller twigs and petioles, and the broadly wedge-shaped bases of the leaves. The margins of the latter are distinctly doubly serrate and their general outline is sub-triangular. The pollen-bearing catkins appear in earliest spring as long festoons from the tips of the more thrifty twigs, two or three of the catkins generally hanging side by side. The seed-bearing catkins are broad and short and stand erect along the sides of the twigs. These develop into ripened seed early in the summer, maturing much in advance of any of the other birches.

The River Birch is a most valuable tree in landscape gardening. It grows rapidly and is especially useful as well as ornamental along the borders of standing or running water, the situations most congenial to it, and where it serves a useful purpose in holding the soil in place. It is comparatively easy to transplant, and in most regions where it grows wild seedlings may readily be found. The tree seldom attains a very great size except in the Southern States, although in the North it often has a trunk diameter of twelve to fifteen inches. The technical name of this species is *Betula nigra*, rather an unfortunate specific name for the Red Birch, especially when we consider that there is in the same regions another species popularly called the Black Birch.

A tree called the Blue Birch is found along the mountains of Northern New England; its technical name is *Betula cærulea*. Professor Sargent says it is the American representative of the European *Betula pendula*.

THE GRAY BIRCH

OVER a large part of the great area which the botanists characterize as the region of the birches, the Gray Birch is the most abundant tree. It springs up everywhere, its minute seeds being scattered far and wide by the wind during many months of the year. It thrives especially on sandy land, where many other trees find it difficult to get a start, and serves a useful purpose as a cover for the growth of more valuable species. It is one of the first trees to take possession of abandoned pasture lands.

The distinguishing characteristics of the Gray Birch are to be found in the triangular leaves with acuminate tips and doubly serrate margins, the slender, pendulous pollen-bearing catkins which are usually solitary on the ends of the twigs, and the erect, linear seed-bearing catkins projecting from the sides of the twigs, as well as in the close white bark with heavy black markings running downward at the junction of the branches.

This tree has long been a favorite with the artists and poets. It has to a peculiar degree that delicate grace of leaf and branch which appeals so strongly to the æsthetic sense. Being found in copses and along the borders of the forests, it forms an important element in our landscape pictures. The varnished leaves reflect the sunlight in a most distinctive manner, while the slender stems cause the position of the blades to be shifted by the slightest breeze. These qualities led Lowell to write—

> " Thy shadow scarce seems shade, thy pattering leaflets
> Sprinkle their gathered sunshine o'er my senses
> And Nature gives me all her summer confidences."

The Gray Birch seldom attains a large size. A height of thirty-five feet and a diameter of eight inches are commonly its extreme dimensions, although occasionally it grows much larger. It is a wonderfully adaptable tree, and is easily modified by its environment. Growing in good soil in open ground, it attains a symmetrical outline of great beauty and delicacy and well deserves more general planting by landscape gardeners. Young trees are easily found in the fields and along the borders of woods and may readily be transplanted.

In addition to the name Gray Birch, this species is often called White Birch, Small White Birch, Poplar Birch, Poverty Birch, and Oldfield Birch. It was happily named *Betula populifolia* by Marsh, on account of the aspen-like effect of its leaves. The species occurs abundantly over a large part of New England and the Middle States.

GRAY BIRCH
BETULA POPULIFOLIA

WHITE, PAPER OR CANOE BIRCH
BETULA PAPYRIFERA

THE WHITE, CANOE BIRCH OR PAPER BIRCH

THE Canoe Birch or Paper Birch is one of the best known trees throughout its range. It is closely associated with our history and literature, and is one of the most beautiful of American trees. It is not so abundant in specimens as the Gray Birch, but attains a much larger size and forms a much more striking feature of the landscape in which it grows. Seen against the dark background of a river or lake, the glistening white trunks of these trees form so striking a picture as to awaken the interest of the most indifferent observer, while a group of young trees growing slenderly erect along the border of the forest forms a picture which is sure to call to mind Coleridge's well-known phrase regarding the English Birch, "The lady of the woods."

Every school-child knows of the usefulness of the bark of this tree in building the canoes of the Indians and early American settlers, and every one who has been so fortunate as to roam the woods where it grows has enjoyed the fascination of peeling off the thin, almost transparent layers of the beautiful bark. In these modern days the trees are largely used in the making of paper pulp, as well as for various purposes in the manufacture of lumber products.

In addition to the loosely peeling, glistening white bark this Birch may be identified by the broadly oval leaves, less narrowly pointed than those of the Gray Birch, with short, stout petioles which are not hairy, and the broad catkins, which are drooping rather than erect. The species is also often called simply the White Birch and was named by Marsh, *Betula papyrifera*.

The Paper Birch is a northern species, occurring from Labrador and the Great Slave Lake region southward as far as New York City, Pennsylvania, Iowa, Nebraska, and Dakota. It is especially abundant in the great wilderness region of Canada, Northern New York and Northern New England, where along the banks of lakes and rivers it is one of the most beautiful and characteristic trees. An interesting form in which the base of the leaves is cordate is found upon the mountains of New England. It has been given the variety name *cordifolia* by Professor Sargent.

> "Give me of your bark, O Birch-tree!
> Of your yellow bark, O Birch-tree!
> Growing by the rushing river
> Tall and stately in the valley!
> I a light canoe will build me,
> Build a swift Cheemaun for sailing,
> That shall float upon the river,
> Like a yellow leaf in Autumn,
> Like a yellow water-lily."
>   LONGFELLOW.

THE EUROPEAN WHITE BIRCH

SUGGESTIONS of the impression which this tree has made upon the masters of English literature must have often come to every one familiar with their writings. The feminine grace and beauty of the trunk, branches and leaves must always appeal to an intelligent observer, and it is not strange that it is the most popular of all ornamental trees, even in America, where we have so many beautiful native kinds. The white bark of the slender trunk, the graceful branches with their long tips "floating at the discretion of the winds," the long-petioled, shining leaves with decorative blades, the interesting flowers and the slender fruit-cones—all these combine to justify the apostrophe of Coleridge:

> " Most beautiful
> Of forest trees—The Lady of the woods."

Like so many plants that have long been in cultivation for landscape purposes, this species has many varieties, perhaps more than any other tree. These varieties exhibit nearly all the variations possible, including divergence in habit of growth, size, shape and color of leaves, length of petiole, and moisture requirements of roots. Mr. Alfred Rehder groups the numerous varieties under two sub-species: the first, which is called the *pendula* group, prefers dry soil and has pendent branches and cones, the bark of the branches being glandular, and smooth leaves which are of the general outline of the normal type except in cut-leaved forms; the second, which is called the *pubescens* group, prefers wet soil and has more upright branches, the bark of which is commonly hairy instead of glandular, leaves which are hairy on the lower surface and cones which may be erect to pendent. Among the more notable varieties of the first group are the Cut-leaved Weeping Birch and the Purple-leaved Birch, while among the more notable varieties of the second group are the Downy-leaved Birch and the Nettle-leaved Birch.

This White Birch is beautiful at any season but it is most exquisite during the brief week in May when the blossoms appear, a condition illustrated in the upper left-hand picture of the plate. The young leaves with their decorative, serrate margins are of a delicate green color that combines charmingly with the more yellow tones of the flowers: from the centre of each group of clustered leaves appears an erect, stalked catkin of the seed-bearing flowers, while from the ends of the twigs droop the pair of slender graceful pollen-bearing catkins. When next the spring reaches that delightful climax of catkin-bloom, be sure you note the unique beauty of these English Birch-Trees.

EUROPEAN WHITE BIRCH
BETULA ALBA

CUT-LEAVED WHITE BIRCH
BETULA ALBA LACINIATA

THE CUT-LEAVED WHITE BIRCH

THE European Birch has been so largely planted in America that it is almost as familiar to us as to the inhabitants of its native country, and even were it not we could easily appreciate the fondness of the poets for it because of our own delight in the matchless beauty of our native white birches, the Gray Birch and the Paper White Birch. The horticultural form known as the Cut-leaved Weeping Birch is the variety most commonly planted in America, and in consequence this has been chosen for illustration in the plate. As will be seen, the play of light and shade on the trunk and larger branches, together with the graceful curves of the pendent twigs, combine to give the tree a most beautiful appearance even when the branches are bare in winter.

This beauty is enhanced, however, to a wonderful degree in early spring, when the tender green of the young leaves pushes out, and the slender, drooping, pollen-bearing catkins develop on the ends of the twigs, and the still more slender, erect seed-bearing catkins push up from the new branches along the sides of the twigs. These two sorts of flowers are well shown in the upper left-hand picture of the plate, while just below is to be seen a twig with a pair of pollen-bearing catkins in their winter condition. After the pollen is shed the larger catkins drop off and the seed-bearing ones begin the development of the seeds. These mature by autumn and are scattered throughout most of the winter months, their form being well shown in the right-hand picture of the plate, in which also may be seen the characteristic incised leaves with their long, slender stems and delicate blades.

This Birch is so thoroughly established as a favorite for ornamental planting that there is no necessity of urging its claims. There is danger, rather, that it will be planted so extensively that the variety and beauty which might be obtained by planting the native Birches along with it will be lost. It certainly has many advantages as an ornamental tree, not the least of which is that it may always be obtained from nurserymen in good condition for transplanting. It is comparatively little injured by insects or fungus diseases, is hardy, and grows quite rapidly, forming from the first an attractive tree. The technical name of this variety is *pendula laciniata:* good nursery-grown trees are commonly offered for sale at a dollar each.

THE SPECKLED ALDER

EVERY plant is a calendar of the year. Through long ages of adaptation it has learned to record the passing season with unerring certainty. The requirements of Nature are relentless: each plant that does not conform to the conditions of its environment is sternly eliminated, as unfit to survive.

None of our native trees or shrubs has learned this lesson with more certainty or expresses it with more grace than the Alders. Standing beside every water-course, they seem to have absorbed through their multitudinous roots the charm inherent in running water, and they attract our regard as inevitably as do the streams themselves. The Alders as a whole are shrubs rather than trees, but a few species sometimes take on the form and size of a tree. The Speckled Alder however, generally remains a shrub. In summer it may be known by its obovate or oval leaves, with the upper surface soft green and the lower surface paler. The margins are very finely serrate, or more or less doubly serrate, and the apex is rounded or obtusely pointed. In autumn these leaves turn slightly yellow or often rusty brown, with the petioles and veins a deep crimson.

After the leaves have fallen the young shoots are seen to have their bark of a brown color more or less covered with a whitish bloom, which in the newest growths may be seen to be due to a resinous exudation mingled with a covering of short hairs. The bark of the twigs in general has numerous white spots which probably gave the species its name of Speckled Alder, as the whitish bloom on the bark probably gave it its other name of Hoary Alder. The vase-shaped leaf-buds have the characteristic form of all the Alder leaf-buds, and the buds of the staminate catkins are generally to be found on the ends of the more vigorous twigs. The undeveloped seed-bearing catkins project downward rather than upward, which is one of the characteristic features of this species.

It is in early spring that the Speckled Alder makes its greatest appeal to one's fancy. The lengthening of the pollen-bearing catkins is the first sign that winter is passing. Even in New England these catkins foretell the coming of spring during bright days in March, and as they hang down in attractive festoons two or three inches long they give the banks of the water-courses an appearance of grace and beauty which is not duplicated during the entire year. The greenish yellow pollen is produced in great abundance and carried by the wind through the branches which bear the much smaller seed-bearing catkins. After the pollen is thus scattered the long catkins drop off and the short ones begin their gradual development into the seed-bearing cones which are so conspicuous on the branches at any season. If in winter you break off a twig bearing some of these cones and shake it over a table you will see the small brown seeds scatter over the surface.

SPECKLED ALDER

SMOOTH ALDER

THE SMOOTH ALDER

IN his delightful essay upon "The Procession of the Flowers" Thomas Wentworth Higginson writes: "The earliest familiar token of the coming season is the expansion of the stiff catkins of the Alder into soft drooping tresses. These are so sensitive that if you pluck them at almost any time during the winter, a few days sunshine will make them open in a vase of water, and thus they eagerly yield to every moment of April warmth. The blossom of the birch is more delicate, that of the willow more showy, but the alders come first. They cluster and dance everywhere upon the bare bough above the water-courses; the blackness of the buds is softened into rich brown and yellow, and as this graceful creature thus comes waving into the spring, it is pleasant to remember that the Norse Eddas fabled the first woman to have been named Embla, because she was created from an Alder bough."

As the Speckled Alder is the prevailing form in the North, so the Smooth Alder is the prevailing form in the South, while in the latitude of Central New England the two intermingle and may be found growing together in varying abundance. The Smooth Alder may be distinguished by the leaves, which are more finely serrate on the margins than those of the Speckled Alder, and also have much rounder or blunter tips: the under surface is generally hairy along the veins. The undeveloped seed-bearing catkins commonly project upward or forward during winter, while those of the Speckled Alder generally hang downward before the blossoming period.

There are various other Alders to be found along ponds and water-courses. One of the most important of these is the European Alder (*A. glutinosa*), which has been so generally planted by man that it is fairly naturalized in many localities. This frequently takes on the shape and size of a tree, and is the commonest tree-like Alder in the Eastern States. Like all the Alders, it flourishes in the wettest soil and so is valuable for landscape gardening in lowlands. In Europe it is called the Black Alder, but in America this name is commonly applied to a very different species—one of the Hollies. There are half-a-dozen horticultural varieties of this European Alder in which the form and color of the leaf is strikingly modified in various ways. The Green or Mountain Alder (*A. viridis*) is a native species found especially in northern or mountainous regions. It is a low shrub, seldom exceeding six feet in height. The Japanese Alder (*A. Japonica*) is said by Mr. Alfred Reyder to be "the largest and perhaps the most beautiful of all Alders." It is a tall tree, generally pyramidal in form.

THE BEECH

FROM time immemorial the European Beech has been celebrated for the denseness of its shade and the usefulness of its wood. In Theocritus we read:

"I ran to meet you as a traveller
Rests from the sun under a shady beech."

And in Virgil we find these lines:

"No wars did men molest
When only beechen bowls were in request."

In these respects the American Beech resembles its European cousin. The thin paper-like leaves are so abundant as to give a most grateful shade, while the hard, tough wood is largely used for manufacturing purposes as well as for fuel. And American artists and poets have found in our trees much the same charm that the European artists and poets have found in theirs. Some of the favorite ornamental trees for planting in America are varieties of the European Beech, notably the familiar Purple-leaved Beech, the Cut-leaved Beech and the Weeping Beech.

The Beech is one of the most characteristic of American trees. In winter the smooth, steel-gray bark of the trunk as well as the long, slender, acutely-pointed buds at once distinguish it. In spring the pollen-bearing and the seed-bearing blossoms, appearing as the leaves develop, differ from those of any other trees, while in summer and autumn the leaves and fruit are both distinctive. The smooth nuts fall from the spiny cases after the first hard frosts, and are filled with a sweet meat which is much esteemed. In former times these nuts formed a large part of the "mast" upon which the wild pigeons fed, and for which the early settlers allowed their swine to roam the woods.

Over a large part of the United States, Beech and Maple formed the prevailing trees of the hardwood forest when the country was settled. Beeches alone often cover considerable forest areas. They occur in a variety of situations, from the sides of mountains of considerable height to the borders of lowland streams, although most abundant on fairly level uplands. The species is distributed from the region of the Great Lakes south to Missouri and Texas, and east to the Atlantic. It is a favorite tree for planting in parks and private estates.

The development of the buds and leaves in spring reveals wonderful color tones in browns and greens, while the young seedlings to be found beneath every bearing tree furnish most interesting studies in the elements of forestry.

BEECH

FAGUS AMERICANA

CHESTNUT
CASTANEA DENTATA

THE CHESTNUT

THROUGHOUT its somewhat limited range the Chestnut tree is one of the best known of all the trees of the forest. It is indigenous from parts of New England and Ontario west to Michigan and south to Indiana and Delaware, extending along the Alleghany mountains to Kentucky, Tennessee and Alabama. It is a particularly handsome and sturdy tree, its characteristic leaves being of a shining green color and having along their margins very distinctive forward-pointing teeth arising from the end of each of the nearly straight veins that run out from the midrib. The short leaf-stems are unusually thick and are enlarged still more at the base. When these leaves fall away they reveal a straight trunked tree with wide spreading branches having the general outline unusually even. The bark of the young twigs is smooth and shining, generally reddish brown or grayish brown in color, and the winter buds are small with comparatively few scales, those along the sides of the twigs projecting at a distinct angle from the stem. The color of the buds varies from greenish brown to chestnut brown. The bark of the larger branches of the trunk is dark gray, much ridged and furrowed. In its best estate the tree reaches a height of a hundred feet and a trunk diameter of six or eight feet. The wood is rather light and soft and seems to be chiefly valuable for fence-posts and railway-ties, being especially resistant to the ill effects of moisture. It is also used for various other purposes. It weighs twenty-eight pounds per cubic foot.

The Chestnut is a handsome tree at any season of the year but it becomes a marvel of graceful beauty in midsummer when the long pollen-bearing catkins push out from the axils of the leaves, giving to the tree a distinctive effect which seems all the more striking on account of the lateness of the season. After a few days of blossoming the pollen-bearing catkins fall off and the rapid development of the seed-bearing flowers begins. The nuts inside their spinous coverings reach maturity so quickly that the first autumnal frosts cause the burs to open and drop and the harvest of the chestnuts is on. The sweet nuts are gathered in great quantities and are sweeter than those of the European chestnut.

The Chestnut tree is commonly planted for shade, ornament and fruit and it has many advantages which render it desirable for this purpose. It is easily propagated from the nuts and young trees may commonly be obtained from nurserymen. It is one of the most promising trees for forestry planting, growing rapidly on nearly all soils except those of limestone formation. For the first thirty years a chestnut tree will increase in height at an average rate of about eighteen inches.

Two other species of Chestnut are often planted for fruit and ornament: one is the European Chestnut, *Castanea sativa*, of which there are many named varieties; and the other is the Japanese Chestnut, *Castanea crenata*, of which there are about a score of named varieties.

The indigenous Chestnut tree has become virtually extinct, as a result of the Chestnut-bark disease.

THE CHINQUAPIN

THE relationship of the Chinquapin to the Chestnut may readily be inferred by comparing the pictures on the plates illustrating the two species: twigs, leaves, flowers and fruits all show a striking resemblance. Both belong to the genus Castanea, and the Chinquapin has well been called the little brother of the Chestnut. The normal shrublike form of the Chinquapin may be seen in the lower picture of the plate which represents part of a group growing at the Arnold Arboretum—a group which has often been cited in illustration of the fact that the species is hardy in Massachusetts, although its northern limit as an indigenous shrub is New Jersey and Pennsylvania, from which states it ranges southward to Florida and Texas. In some parts of this great area it develops into a tree form forty or fifty feet high, though more commonly it is a shrub which spreads by underground stems into bushy thickets. These shrubs are remarkable however, in that they bear the small chestnut-like fruits when only about a yard high and in such abundance that these sweet chestnuts are commonly sold in Southern cities

In the Cyclopedia of Horticulture the useful qualities of the Chinquapin for landscape gardeners are summarized in these words: "Useful for planting on dry and rocky slopes; attractive when in flower and again in fall, with its abundant light green burs among the dark foliage." The flowers appear toward midsummer; the pollen-bearing blossoms are in the long spikes shown on the plate, while the small seed-bearing flowers with their projecting stigmas are shown on the twig between these spikes. The shrubs become especially attractive when the foliage changes to its yellow hue in autumn.

On the Pacific Coast there grows a beautiful tree called the Golden-leaved Chestnut (*Castanopsis chrysophylla*) which is closely related to the Chinquapin and the Chestnut. In its best development it reaches a height of one hundred and fifty feet and a trunk diameter of ten feet, but commonly it is of course much smaller, and often is a mere shrub, the latter condition prevailing along the upper mountain slopes. It is notable for the beauty of its foliage, which has the peculiar character of remaining on the branches for two or three years, turning yellow before falling so that the branches commonly show both green and golden leaves. In addition the under surface of the leaves is "coated with golden yellow persistent scales." The sweet nuts are borne in spiny burs resembling those of the Chinquapin. The tree form is not hardy in cold climates, but the shrubby form from the higher altitudes is so much hardier that it is worth trying on the Eastern coast

CHINQUAPIN
CASTANEA PUMILA

RED OAK
QUERCUS RUBRA

BEECH AND OAK FAMILY

FAGACEÆ

THE RED OAK

THE Red Oak is a typical example of the group with bristle-pointed lobes on the leaves and with acorns that require two seasons to reach maturity. It is an abundant and widely distributed species, well known to nearly every one and both in summer and winter is one of the most beautiful of our native trees. It is readily distinguished from the somewhat similar Black or Yellow Oak by its much larger acorns, its straighter branches, and its pinkish-gray inner bark. It is distinguished from the Scarlet Oak by its larger acorns, with a cup much broader than high, and by the broader blades of the leaves, the lobes of which generally are not so deeply cut as those of the Scarlet Oak. There are two forms of leaves, one broad with rather shallow sinuses; the other slender with deep sinuses. In winter the Red Oak is characterized by a general straightness of limb and smoothness of shining bark that give it a very attractive appearance. The youngest shoots commonly have column-like ridges that lead to the shield-shaped leaf-scars on elevated bases. The buds are narrowly conical and generally sharply pointed, the scales being slightly downy but much less so than are the scales on the winter buds of the Black or Yellow Oak.

The wood of the Red Oak is hard and rather coarse-grained, weighing forty-one pounds per cubic foot and being light reddish brown in color. It is used largely for fuel as well as for furniture and many other purposes. The tree commonly reaches a height of less than a hundred feet but sometimes specimens one hundred and fifty feet high are found. The trunk diameter is frequently three or four feet, the largest trees being found in the more central portions of its range, especially in the northern part of the basin of the Ohio River. Its range extends from Nova Scotia, New Brunswick and Quebec west to Kansas and Nebraska, and south to Virginia and Tennessee, and along the slopes of the Appalachian Mountains to Georgia.

The Red Oak is one of the most desirable trees for shade and ornament. When once successfully transplanted it grows very rapidly and is an admirable tree for street purposes. About its only serious insect enemy is the twig-pruner, which sometimes causes considerable numbers of twigs to fall to the ground beneath the tree. If these are all gathered and burned, however, the insects will be destroyed and their injury checked. This species grows more rapidly than the other oaks, and thrives best in well-drained sandy clay soils where there is a fair amount of moisture. The bitter acorns are seldom molested by squirrels so that for forestry purposes they can be planted directly in the field with little fear that they will be dug up, as are too often the acorns of the White Oak.

THE PIN OAK

THE Pin Oak is one of the most characteristic species of the Red Oak group. Its preference for low grounds is shown by its other common names of Swamp Spanish Oak and Water Oak, as well as by its technical name, *Quercus palustris.* It occurs, especially in swamps and along the margins of low-banked rivers, over a great region extending from Massachusetts to Ontario and Minnesota, and south to Kansas, Missouri, Kentucky, and Tennessee. It is only locally found in New England and then is generally of a small size, but in the region of the Ohio River it is abundant and sometimes reaches a height of more than a hundred feet.

The character of younger trees as they grow more or less in the open is well shown in the straight-trunked tree illustrated on the plate, in which it will be noticed that the secondary branches are more slender and abundant than in the case of most of the Oaks pictured on the other plates. Michaux has said that these intermingled twigs give the tree at a distance the appearance of being full of pins, and he adds, "This singular disposition renders it distinguishable at first sight in winter and is perhaps the cause of its being called Pin Oak."

Just above this picture of the tree may be seen a twig bearing the long catkins of pollen-producing flowers at the base of the new season's growth, and the small, stalked seed-producing flowers in the axils of the leaves above. The latter do not mature until the end of the second season, when they form broad acorns borne in wide, shallow cups which are one of the most characteristic features of the species. These broad acorns and shallow cups serve as a ready means of distinguishing the Pin Oak from the Red Oak.

On account of the brilliant green of the foliage and the slender habit of the tree this species is especially desirable for ornamental planting, and it has also the advantage that it is offered for sale by many nurserymen. Its chief disadvantage is found in the fact that the leaves are occasionally subject to the attack of gall-producing insects. It has proved particularly desirable as a street tree in the City of Washington.

PIN OAK
QUERCUS PALUSTRIS

SCARLET OAK
QUERCUS COCCINEA

THE SCARLET OAK

THIS is one of the most beautiful members of the great Oak family and it is especially notable for the brilliant beauty of its shining autumn foliage. It belongs to the group of Oaks that have bristle-pointed leaves, being similar in some respects to the Red Oak on the one hand and the Black Oak on the other. It is distinguished from the former by its much smaller acorns with hemispherical rather than flat cups, and from the latter by the fact that its inner bark is not yellow. The leaves are normally deeply incised, the rounded depressions between the lobes extending nearly to the midrib.

The blossoms of the Scarlet Oak appear rather early in spring when the leaves are about half grown. They are similar to those of the other Oaks, the pollen-bearing flowers being arranged in long catkins at the base of the new season's growth, and the red seed-bearing flowers being arranged singly in the axils of the young leaves. The stigmas of the latter are very large and spreading, an obvious method of increasing the chances of receiving some of the wind-blown pollen grains. The acorns from these flowers require two years for their development, and though small they are very attractive in form and coloring. Some of them are sessile, others have short stalks. They are borne in beautiful little cups which generally reach half way to the tip of the acorn, being thin-edged at the top and having the scales pressed closely against each other. If the fancy of the poet is true, these would be excellent cups for those elves of which he wrote:

"All their elves for fear
Crept into acorn cups and hid themselves."

In the more northern parts of its range the Scarlet Oak seldom attains a greater height than thirty feet or a greater trunk diameter than two feet, but further south it frequently attains a larger size. Its range extends from New England to Ontario, Michigan, and Minnesota, south to Illinois and the District of Columbia, and along the slopes of the Alleghany Mountains to North Carolina and Tennessee. It is especially abundant in the coast region from Massachusetts to New Jersey, and is most likely to be found in dry soils.

The Scarlet Oak is desirable for planting in parks and private grounds on account of its brilliant autumnal coloring and the general beauty of the tree at other seasons. It grows readily from seed but the young trees are likely to be unsymmetrical, so that it is not especially desirable for planting in rows along streets or driveways where uniformity of appearance is required. It is quite free from insect or fungus enemies and grows rapidly.

THE BLACK OAK OR YELLOW-BARK OAK

IN its leaves the Black Oak or Yellow-bark Oak bears a general resemblance to the Red Oak, from which, however, it is at once distinguished at any season of the year by its orange-yellow inner bark, easily found by cutting out a bit of bark on the trunk or one of the larger limbs with a penknife. In autumn it is readily known by its smaller acorns in cups that extend half way to the top of the nut, and are not broad and shallow as are those of the Red Oak. There are two forms of leaves: one, the broad leaves with rather shallow lobes like the typical leaves of the Red Oak, the other, narrower leaves with rather deeply cut lobes suggestive of the typical leaves of the Scarlet Oak though not so deeply cut. The yellow inner bark, however, will at once distinguish either form of the Black Oak.

When the handsome leaves of this tree have fallen away they reveal, in the case of specimens in open situations, a splendid tree with the interlacing branches very irregularly curved and with a wide-spreading, rounded outline which is very attractive. This character of the tree is well shown in the noble specimen illustrated on the plate. The bark of the young shoots is light grayish or reddish brown, more or less roughened by slightly raised oval dots. The rather large leaf-scars are on slightly elevated bases and the large sub-conical buds are densely covered with a light brown down which is quite characteristic.

The Black Oak comes into blossom soon after the young leaves begin to develop. The blossoming conditions are well represented in the upper left-hand picture on the plate, where the long, pollen-bearing catkins are shown hanging down from the base of the new season's shoot, and the stalked seed-bearing flowers are shown in the axils of the new leaves, the size of which at blossoming-time is indicated in the single leaf with its long, bristle-pointed lobes. For a few days these blossoming Oak trees present a striking appearance. The young leaves are densely woolly on both surfaces and are generally more or less reddish on the upper surface.

The Black Oak is found as an indigenous tree from New England to Minnesota, west to Kansas and Texas, and south to Florida. Its value for planting as an ornamental tree is lessened by the fact that it is often seriously attacked by the gall insects that make the so-called Oak Apples, as well as by the tendency of the trees to become unsightly through the persistence of dead branches.

BLACK OAK — YELLOW-BARK OAK
QUERCUS VELUTINA

BEAR OR SCRUB OAK
QUERCUS NANA—QUERCUS ILICIFOLIA

THE BEAR OAK OR SCRUB OAK

AMONG the smaller Oaks which are more likely to be found as shrubs than trees the Bear or Scrub Oak is one of the most abundant in the Eastern States. It is said to have received its common name because the early settlers observed that the bears fed freely upon the acorns. It is easily distinguished by its characteristic bristle-pointed leaves, several typical forms of which are shown on the plate. These leaves turn reddish brown or brown in autumn and many of them remain upon the branches throughout the winter.

The young twigs of this species are generally somewhat more cylindrical than those of the larger Oaks, and have rather smooth bark of a grayish or brownish color. The small brown buds are rounded or bluntly conical, with closely imbricated scales which are covered with a slight pubescence.

The conditions at the time of blossoming of this species are admirably shown in the upper left-hand picture of the plate. As will be seen, the blossoms appear when the leaves are about one-third grown. After shedding their pollen the pollen-bearing catkins drop away, while the young acorns slowly develop, requiring two seasons to reach maturity. These full-grown acorns are generally quite small, their average length being half an inch and the shape usually being broad and rounded. The cups are quite deep, with closely imbricated scales, and are borne in stalked clusters along the sides of the smaller branches. In the larger picture on the plate the fully-developed acorns are shown, and in the axils of the leaves of the longest branch projecting downward there are also shown some young acorns which were simply blossoms the previous spring.

The Bear Oak is most abundant in rather barren, sandy regions along the Atlantic coast. It is characteristic of that part of Massachusetts where Thoreau's Walden was located, and appears to have been one of his favorite trees, being often mentioned under the name "scrub oak." It extends from New England southward to Pennsylvania, and along the slopes of the Alleghany Mountains to Virginia. It does not range very far west from the Atlantic coast. As a tree it seldom attains a height of more than twenty feet or a trunk diameter of more than six inches. In ornamental planting it is chiefly useful on large estates where a shrubby growth is desired on a sandy slope or along a rocky hillside.

THE SHINGLE OAK

THE Shingle Oak is a good illustration of an important group of Oaks in which the leaves are narrow and have entire margins. For this reason they suggest the Willows rather than the Oaks, and one accustomed only to the characteristic forms of the leaves shown by the various White, Black or Red Oaks almost needs the reassuring presence of the acorns to be convinced that such leaves really belong to Oak trees. In the case of the present species the leaves suggest those of the Mountain Laurel to an extent that has led it often to be called the Laurel Oak. But as this name is also applied to another form common in the South it would be better to drop it in connection with the Shingle Oak: the form referred to is called the Water Oak by Sargent; its technical name is *Quercus laurifolia*, which apparently justifies the Cyclopedia of Horticulture in its use of Laurel Oak as a common name, just as the name *Quercus imbricaria* indicates that Shingle Oak is an appropriate name for the present species.

The Shingle Oak reaches its maximum development near the junction of the Ohio and Mississippi Rivers, from whence it radiates in various directions: it extends north to Michigan and Wisconsin, east to Pennsylvania, Georgia, and Alabama, west to Missouri and Kansas, and to Tennessee. Outside these limits the tree has often been planted for shade and ornament, the species being hardy as far north as central New England. The tallest trees are one hundred feet high, but generally they are only about half as high. "The leaves of the Shingle Oak," writes a good observer, "are very narrow, almost linear at first, with their edges so straightly revolute that they almost touch each other. They are slightly hairy, the ground color yellowish green with a purple tinge. The fresh twigs are flushed with red on the upper side where most exposed to the light. The young leaves stand out stiffly from the ends of the branchlets, studding them with sharply outlined stellate clusters. Being so narrow, the foliage is very open and one can see through the tree-top in almost any direction, so that the tree has an appearance quite distinct from other oaks." The acorns are small and broad for their height, and are held in wide, shallow cups.

The typical form of the group to which the Shingle Oak belongs is the Willow Oak. The leaves of this tree are very slender, their outlines closely resembling those of Willow leaves. The Willow Oak grows along the margins of swamps and water-courses in the same sort of situations that the Willow prefers, and occurs from New York southward to Florida, and westward to Texas. Although it occurs chiefly in states that touch the sea or gulf coast, it is found along fresh rather than salt waters.

SHINGLE OAK — LAUREL OAK

FAGACEÆ

WHITE OAK
QUERCUS ALBA

THE WHITE OAK

O F all the trees of the forest in which man has seen the qualities of life, the Oak seems always to have been the symbol of sturdy strength. The literature of all ages abounds in allusions to this quality of the tree, which has perhaps been best expressed in those well-known lines of Virgil:

"Jove's own tree,
That holds the woods in awful sovereignty;
Nor length of ages lasts his happy reign.
And lives of mortal men contend in vain.
Full in the midst of his own strength he stands,
Stretching his brawny arms and leafy hands,
His shade protects the plants; his heart the hills commands."

To many Americans it is probable that the White Oak generally represents most typically those qualities which have made the European Oak so prominent in literature. This is one of the most widely distributed of our Oaks, and its wide-spreading branches have been associated with the early life of great numbers of our people. Whether in summer, autumn, spring or winter the tree always has a distinctive and majestic beauty that serves to endear it to all that come under its influence.

Our native Oaks are readily divided into two great groups: in the first of these the lobes of the leaf are rounded and the acorns mature in a single season; in the second the lobes of the leaf are pointed and the acorns require two seasons to mature. As will be seen by reference to the plate, the White Oak, is a typical example of the first group, which includes also the Swamp White Oak, the Chestnut Oak, the Burr Oak, and the Post Oak. Among these trees the White Oak is distinguished by the fact that the sinuses between the lobes are very deep, commonly extending more than half way toward the midrib. This fact gives the species a distinctive character that enables one easily to recognize it. The upper surface of the leaf is yellow green, the under surface being considerably lighter. The rather small acorns are held in, shallow cups, singly or in groups of two or three at the end of a very short stalk, which, however, is often lacking.

The White Oak ranges on the north from Maine to Minnesota, cn the west to Nebraska, Kansas, and Texas, and on the south to Florida. It is a valuable tree for landscape planting, although it grows slowly and is rather difficult to transplant successfully. It is especially likely to be found on rather dry soils of sandy loam and it generally does not take kindly to wet situations. It is most beautiful when growing in the open, as in the case of the pasture oaks of New England, which are so beautiful, especially in autumn when their foliage changes to a rich red color.

THE POST OAK

THE Post Oak may at once be known by the very unusual form of the leaves, with their large rounded or squarish lobes, the three terminal lobes being the largest and giving a very unusual appearance to the leaf. It belongs to the group of the White Oaks, the lobes of the leaf not being bristle-pointed and the acorns maturing the first season.

The Post Oak is essentially a Southern species, reaching its northern limit in Southern Massachusetts, from whence it extends southward to Florida and westward to Kansas and Texas. In the more northern parts of its range it is a comparatively small and unattractive tree, but in the lower Mississippi Valley and other southern regions it attains a large size and often forms the prevailing element in the Oak forests. The bark of the trunk is finely checked with numerous vertical furrows of a dark grayish or grayish-brown color. The young branches are notably hairy and bear downy buds. The wood is hard and firm, weighing fifty-two pounds per cubic foot and being especially desirable for fence-posts on account of its slowness of decay when placed in the ground. Presumably this fact has given it its common name. The wood is also used for fuel and for railway ties.

The Post Oak comes into flower when the leaves are quite small. The pollen-bearing catkins have a generally yellow color, while the seed-bearing flowers commonly have a reddish appearance due to the very large red stigmas. The latter are clustered in the axils of the leaves and mature in the same season into unusually small acorns with rather shallow cups, the general characteristics of which are well shown on the plate. As the young leaves develop, their upper surface is distinctly dark red in color and their lower surface orange brown on account of the dense woolly covering of hairs of this color. As the leaves reach full size the reddish upper surface gives place to a deep dark-green color and the orange-brown under surface becomes much paler, the hairs spreading out through the increase in size of the leaf, so that they appear as a pale pubescence. The leaves remain upon the trees well into the winter, becoming a deep brown color which is often preceded by a yellow tone.

On account of its distinctive characteristics one or two Post Oaks would be a desirable addition to a landed estate, but it does not seem to be an especially desirable tree for ornamental planting in the North. It is difficult to transplant, and grows slowly. The distinctive characters of the leaves may easily be obtained by planting some of the acorns in the location where the trees are to develop.

BUR OAK — MOSSY CUP OAK
QUERCUS MACROCARPA

THE BUR OAK OR MOSSY-CUP OAK

NONE of the Oaks are marked by more distinctive characters than the Bur Oak or Mossy-cup Oak. The form of the leaves is unique, there being on each side near the middle a deep, rounded sinus that reaches almost to the midrib, which practically divides the leaf into two rather distinct parts, the apical part commonly having curious squarish lobes and the basal part having more or less triangular lobes. When once this distinctive feature of the tree is fixed in mind there will be no difficulty in recognizing the species at a glance. The fruit is also unique, the broad, smooth nut being nearly enclosed by the curious mossy cup which serves to give the tree one of its common names; and many of the younger branches also show a distinctive character in the corky ridges along their sides.

The Bur Oak is found as an indigenous tree over a great region extending from New Brunswick and Nova Scotia to Ontario and Manitoba on the north, to Montana, Nebraska, Kansas, and Texas on the west, and to Pennsylvania, Tennessee, and Massachusetts on the south. It appears to be a tree of the Great Plains regions of the West and Northwest, being found most abundantly in the rich soil along river valleys. It is a prevailing species in the so-called "Oak openings" of some of the Northwestern States. Near the junction of the Ohio and Mississippi Rivers many of the trees attain an enormous size, reaching a height of more than a hundred and fifty feet and a trunk diameter of six or seven feet; but in most regions, especially in the Northeast, it is usually a very much smaller tree and sometimes little more than a shrub. The mode of branching of medium-sized trees growing in the open is well shown in the lower picture of the plate. As will be seen, there is a general tendency of the larger branches to grow upward, and the smaller branches tend even more markedly in the same direction. The bark of the trunk is dark gray and is furrowed by vertical ridges.

The Bur Oak blossoms about the same time as the other Oaks, when its earliest leaves are half grown, and the large acorns develop the same season. In shape and size the fruits vary greatly, but the cup is unmistakable on account of the mossy fringe around its upper surface. This is an interesting tree for ornamental planting, generally quite free from insect or fungus enemies, and like so many of the other Oaks most easily propagated from acorns planted where the trees are to develop. It thrives to best advantage on rich, moist, well-drained soil, in open sunlight. It grows about as rapidly as the White Oak, considerably more slowly than the Red Oak. Its wood is similar to that of the first named species.

THE SWAMP WHITE OAK

THE Swamp White Oak is at once distinguished from the White Oak by the fact that the sinuses between the lobes of the leaves are very shallow, giving to the blade a broad effect which is quite different from that of the other species. The acorns also are larger and each is held in a much deeper cup which extends nearly half way to the apex of the nut. As the name indicates, this tree is most likely to be found in rather damp situations, being especially common along the borders of swamps and the banks of streams. The upper surface of the blade of the leaf is of a shining dark yellow-green color, while the under surface is light green and finely downy. In autumn the leaves turn yellow brown or brown and remain upon the twigs far into the winter or even until spring.

The characteristic growth of the branches, as it is revealed in winter, is well shown in the specimen pictured on the plate. Many of the smaller branches grow downward in a manner that gives the tree a rough, rugged appearance, even for an Oak. The bark of the trunk of good-sized trees is a dark grayish color, made rougher by scales and striations which led one authority to call this "the untidy oak." In younger trees and on larger branches there are many loose scales which are quite characteristic. Like so many other trees this species in the Ohio Valley attains an enormous size, although in other regions it seldom reaches a height of more than sixty feet or a trunk diameter of more than three feet. One famous tree in New York however had a circumference of twenty-seven feet.

The flowers of the Swamp White Oak appear in May when the leaves are about one-third grown. The pollen-bearing blossoms are in long catkins, clustered together at the base of the new season's shoots in a way well shown in the picture. A great amount of pollen is shed by these catkins to be scattered far and wide by the wind, some of it fertilizing the red stigmas of the seed-bearing flowers. As the leaves unfold they are of a greenish or bronze-green hue seldom showing the red tints so characteristic of many of the other oaks.

This species ranges from Maine and Vermont west to Ontario, Michigan, and Iowa; south to Arkansas, Kentucky, and the District of Columbia, and extends along the slopes of the Appalachian Mountains to Northern Georgia. It is a valuable tree for street and ornamental planting, especially in wet situations. It grows rather rapidly and although furnishing a home for a great variety of insects it is seldom disfigured by them.

In the South the Basket Oak or Cow Oak (*Quercus Michauxii*) occupies much the same place that the Swamp White Oak does in the North. It is an abundant and valuable tree, and by many authorities is considered to be the Southern representative of the Swamp White Oak.

ROCK CHESTNUT OAK
QUERCUS PRINUS

THE ROCK CHESTNUT OAK

THE Chestnut Oak receives its common name on account of the general resemblance of the leaf to that of the Chestnut, a fact which enables one to distinguish the species from the other Oaks at a glance. It belongs to the group of White Oaks in which the leaf lobes are rounded and the acorns mature the first season. It is essentially an Eastern species, and is rather a local tree over a large part of its range, which extends from Maine to Maryland and along the mountains to Georgia and Alabama. It reaches westward to Lakes Champlain and Erie, and to Kentucky. It is generally an Oak of the highlands, being found chiefly along the higher banks of rivers though sometimes it grows at the water's edge. It forms a predominant element of the forest along the bases of the mountains in the southern part of its range. It is in this region that the trees reach their largest size and sometimes attain a height of a hundred feet and a trunk diameter of six feet. More commonly, however, a full-sized tree reaches a height of sixty feet with a trunk diameter of but three feet, and very often the trees are much smaller than this, especially in dry, hilly situations. Good-sized trees commonly show pronounced and distinctive ridges in the bark of the trunk.

The young leaves are of a beautiful yellow-green or bronze color, brilliantly shining on the upper surface but covered with a dense pubescence on the lower surface. As they reach maturity they are rather thick, even for an Oak leaf, and on the upper surface are of a shining dark yellow-green color, while on the lower surface they are much paler and slightly pubescent. Before falling in autumn they change first to yellow and then to a deep yellow-brown color. The acorns have short stalks, these stalks being shorter than the rather long petioles of the leaf. They are commonly borne singly or sometimes in pairs and are of a beautiful rounded shape with the cup extending about one-third of the distance towards the tip of the nut, the scales being indicated by the slightly roughened appearance, which is more pronounced toward the base. The kernel of this acorn is whitish in color and sweetish in taste, and is a favorite article of food with the squirrels.

The Chestnut Oak, which is also called the Rock Chestnut Oak, is an unusually attractive tree for ornamental planting, and it has the special advantage for this purpose that it may be more readily transplanted than most of the Oaks. It grows rapidly and is seldom attacked by enemies and is an excellent tree for streets and avenues.

The Yellow Chestnut Oak (*Quercus acuminata*) is a closely related form in which the tips of the leaves are more acuminate. It is widely distributed throughout the eastern region of the United States extending from Massachusetts west to Nebraska and south to Louisiana and Alabama. In the basin of the Wabash river it reaches a height of one hundred and sixty feet.

THE CHINQUAPIN OAK

THE Chinquapin Oak is a shrubby species which is readily identified by its leaves and fruits: the former have somewhat the appearance of Chestnut leaves, though the teeth along the margins are not so well developed; the latter are commonly borne on short stalks, and have tuberculate, close-fitting cups, each inclosing nearly half its acorn. The species is sometimes called the Scrub Chestnut Oak, probably from the resemblance of the small leaves to those of the Chestnut. The thickets are brought about through underground stems that radiate in various directions and send up new shoots. The blossoms develop late in spring when the leaves are pushing out, the pollen-bearing flowers being at the base of the new shoot and the seed-bearing ones in the axils of the new leaves.

The Chinquapin Oak is especially likely to be found on barren sandy soils. It occurs from New England to Alabama on the east, and from Minnesota to Texas on the West. Miss Keeler states that in Kansas and Missouri it becomes tree-like. A suggestion for its use in forestry has been made by George B. Emerson, who says: "Where this little oak constitutes the principal growth it might easily be made to perform an important service. If the seeds of the pitch pine, the red Cedar, the larch, or some of the valuable oaks, were placed at the right season, an inch or less beneath the surface of the soil, they would spring up under its shade, and be protected by it from sun and wind, until they were large enough to need no further protection; after which it might be grubbed up or left to die gradually in the shade." Like the Bear Oak, this species produces abundant crops of acorns.

Many of the oaks are notable for furnishing a supply of material for tannin. In California there is a tree so remarkable in this respect that it is called the Tan-bark Oak or sometimes the California Chestnut Oak. It seems to be a connecting link between the Chestnuts and the Oaks and is known technically as *Pasania densiflora*. The leaves are very similar to those of the Chestnut and the pollen-bearing flowers are born in stiff rather than pendent catkins. In size it varies from a low shrub, which has been given the variety name *echinoides* by Professor Sargent, to a tree nearly a hundred feet high. It occurs in the coast regions of Oregon and California.

FAGACEÆ

LIVE OAK

QUERCUS VIRGINIANA

BEECH AND OAK FAMILY

THE LIVE OAK

MANY of the Oaks in the North retain their brown, dead leaves through the winter months, but the Live Oak has received its common name because it retains its green leaves until the appearance of a new crop the following season. To the uninitiated however, these seem not at all like Oak leaves, having rather elliptical outlines, suggestive of a Willow leaf, the margins being generally smooth, though occasionally broken by short teeth along the terminal half. The thick leaf-stems are very short, but the pairs or larger groups of slender, sharply-pointed acorns are borne on extraordinarily long stalks, sometimes reaching a length of five inches. The tree is especially remarkable for its spread of branches: though it rarely reaches a greater height than fifty feet it sometimes has a horizontal spread of thrice that distance. Large trees have a trunk diameter of four feet, the base of the trunk commonly being swollen or buttressed in a curious and characteristic manner. The wood has long been noted for its strength and hardness, and in the early history of the United States was considered so necessary in ship-building that large tracts in the South covered by these trees were set aside by the Government for the exclusive use of the Navy.

In a general way the Live Oak may be said to be indigenous in the South Atlantic and the Gulf States. It is especially abundant along the coast, and will grow just above salt water, a dwarf form found in such situations having been described by Professor Sargent as bearing acorns when only a foot high. The species is justly esteemed as a shade and ornamental tree in Southern cities, it having the advantages of ease of transplanting, rapidity of growth, long life, and spreading branches. It is a favorite host of the famous Spanish moss of the South, which soon clothes the branches with long festoons that add to the picturesque effect though it conceals to a great extent the really beautiful foliage of the Live Oak. Of the effect of sudden showers upon these festooned oaks Mr. J. Horace McFarland writes: "One day a walk about Savannah, which city has many splendid Live Oaks in its parks and squares, involved me in a sudden shower, when, presto! the Weeping Willow of the North was reincarnated before my eyes, for the falling rain turned the dingy moss pendants of the Live Oak to the whitish green that makes the Willow such a delightful color note in early spring. I have been thankful often for that shower, for it gave me a better feeling about the Live Oak and made me admire the Weeping Willow."

THE WHITE ELM

NO tree can successfully dispute the claim of the White Elm to be the favorite species of the American people. Widely distributed, it is universally admired for its grace and beauty at all seasons of the year. It is hardy, easily transplanted, and a rapid grower, but unfortunately is often seriously injured by various insect enemies, especially the destructive Elm-Leaf beetle.

In winter the White Elm is easily recognized by the long, slender, drooping branches sent out from the generally vase-shaped tree, the branches being smooth and slender and the buds having no downy covering. In early spring, when the dense clusters of flowers line the twigs, the tree takes on a most interesting appearance, which becomes even more so a little later when the flat, round, whitish, winged fruits replace the reddish blossoms, and at about the same time the tiny leaves gradually unfold, adding to the grace of the filmy fringe with which the smaller branches are adorned. Even when the leaves attain their full size the tree loses little in its graceful appearance, each leaf being finely modelled with doubly serrate margins and sides of unequal size. In autumn at the time they fall their color changes to a beautiful clear yellow.

There are two situations in which this Elm is especially attractive: first, where the great trees line each side of a village or city street, their twigs forming an arch that gives grateful shade to the passer-by, and second, where the trees stand singly or in clusters along a fertile river valley, adding an incomparable element of grace to the landscape. In such situations the most indifferent observer must perforce admire the distinctive beauty of these trees.

In the older settled regions of the United States there are many great elms having special interest on account of their historical associations. The most notable of these is the famous Washington Elm, under which the Father of his Country assumed command of the Continental Army.

One of the most interesting tree sights of early summer is that of the thousands of tiny elm-trees that spring up from the seed which shortly before was scattered broadcast by the wind. Where the bearing trees are numerous these little seedlings will make a veritable lawn even of the gutters of city streets, and one can easily gather for transplanting all the seedlings that could be desired. In a year or two those thus transplanted would be large enough to set out in permanent situations. Every one knows that the White Elm is desirable for planting throughout New England and the Middle States, and the Forest Service states, that it is " especially well suited for prairie and plains " plantations, although in such regions the soil should be well prepared before the trees are set out.

WHITE ELM — AMERICAN ELM
ULMUS AMERICANA

ROCK ELM — CORK ELM
ULMUS THOMASI—ULMUS RACEMOSA

THE ROCK ELM OR CORK ELM

THE very striking peculiarity which distinguishes the Cork Elm from the other native species is clearly shown in the tree pictured on the plate, as well as in the branch from which the leaf-bearing twig arises. The peculiar corky ridges upon the secondary branches give the tree a very different appearance from that of any other, and enables one always to distinguish this species with ease and certainty. The tree is especially likely to be found along high river banks or in rather dry, rich soils, and is irregularly distributed throughout a rather limited range, extending from Quebec and Ontario on the north, south through parts of New England and New York to New Jersey, and west to Wisconsin, Nebraska, and Missouri. According to Professor Sargent it is most abundant in Michigan and Ontario.

In its best estate the Cork Elm will bear comparison in size and dignity with the noble American Elm, although it lacks some of the grace of the latter species. The tree occasionally reaches a height of a hundred feet and a trunk diameter of three feet, although generally it is much smaller. The grayish bark of the trunk is marked by numerous vertical fissures, between which are many large, loosened scales. The winter buds are hairy, resembling in this respect those of the Slippery Elm.

In regions where the tree is abundant the wood is used for a great variety of manufacturing purposes, it being heavy, hard, close-grained and weighing forty-five pounds per cubic foot. On account of the valuable qualities of the wood the species is sometimes called the Hickory Elm, and on account of the fact that it often grows upon rocky ledges it is sometimes called the Cliff Elm.

Like the other members of the genus the Cork Elm blossoms very early in spring, before the leaves push out, but unlike the other species the blossoms are borne in distinct racemes, a fact which led to the technical name, *Ulmus racemosa*. These racemes shortly develop into the hairy fruits represented in the upper left-hand picture of the plate, these fruits being somewhat larger than those of the American Elm and smaller than those of the Slippery Elm.

This species has been rather extensively planted for shade and ornament in cities along the Pacific coast. It proved to be of rapid growth and desirable except for the fact that it sent its roots long distances in search of water and from these roots there came up numerous suckers that were difficult to destroy, especially when the tree itself had been cut down. A writer in The Garden Magazine says that on account of gardens ruined by these suckers the Cork Elm is no longer planted.

THE RED ELM OR SLIPPERY ELM

THE Slippery Elm is generally to be distinguished at a distance from the American Elm by its much less graceful habit of growth, the upper branches projecting more or less straightly out instead of drooping in graceful curves as do those of the American species. The leaves of the Slippery Elm when rubbed by the finger-tips are rough in two directions, which is also a distinctive character, while of course the mucilaginous inner bark, which gives the tree its commonest name, will always characterize it. In winter it may be identified by the downy buds and in spring by the key-fruits or samaras, which are much larger than those of the White Elm.

The Red Elm is a widely distributed species, being found indigenous from the valley of the St. Lawrence west to North Dakota and south to Florida and Texas. It usually does not attain a great height, and the head of the tree spreads out widely for the size of the trunk. The trees grow rapidly from seed, and have one advantage over the American Elm, in that they are less subject to attack by insect enemies.

In early spring the large, rounded, dark brown, downy flower-buds burst forth into reddish blossoms, which are borne in clusters along the sides of the twigs. In respect to the presence of stamens and pistils these flowers vary greatly; in some, stamens only are present; in others, pistils only; while in still others both stamens and pistils may be found. These three sorts of flowers often occur upon the same tree. Soon after the flowers have gone by, the characteristic fruits develop. These are flat samaras, round or oval in shape, with the wall over the seed coated with fine hairs, but having the wing of the fruit smooth and not hairy along its margins, as is that of the White Elm. These fruits are widely distributed by the wind.

The Slippery Elm is sometimes also called the Moose Elm, and by the Indians, by whom the inner bark was used for throat troubles, it was called "oo-hoosk-ah," meaning "it slips."

It is probable that as the troubles from insect enemies to the White Elm become more marked this species will be more largely planted for shade and ornament. It is easily raised from the seed, and deserves more attention than it has hitherto received.

RED ELM — SLIPPERY ELM
ULMUS FULVA — ULMUS PUBESCENS

ENGLISH ELM
ULMUS CAMPESTRIS

ELM FAMILY

THE ENGLISH ELM

THE tree which has been very generally planted in New England and some other parts of America under the name of English Elm is the common Elm of Central and Southern Europe, where it has been planted as an ornamental tree from time immemorial. It was introduced into America by some of the earliest settlers and is said to have been first planted by a wheelwright who desired the wood for making hubs, for which purpose the wood of the tree has long been famous. Some of the most celebrated and beautiful trees of this species growing in America are those on Boston Common, a noble group of them being represented in the plate. As will be noticed, the habit of growth is quite different from that of our more graceful American Elm, and the tree when growing alone in the open often takes on an appearance which at a little distance reminds one of an Oak. The largest of those on the Mall in Boston Harbor was measured in 1844 by Professor Asa Gray and Mr. George B. Emerson and found to have a circumference of eleven feet and two inches, five feet from the ground. Some other English Elms which were formerly growing near Park Street Church were said to have been planted in 1762 and in 1826 to have measured nine feet in circumference at four feet from the ground. Some other Elms in Roxbury, Massachusetts, after having been planted fifty years, measured eight feet and eleven inches at three feet from the ground. These facts indicate that, like our own White Elm, the European species grows very rapidly. As an ornamental tree it also has the decided advantage that it retains its green foliage for a considerably later period in autumn than do our native species. There are a great many horticultural varieties of the English Elm.

As will be seen from the picture on the plate, the flowers of the English Elm are quite similar to those of the American, while the fruit is much larger and of a different shape. The foliage is less sharply and deeply serrate on the margins. The leaves of this tree were used in olden times as food for cattle by the Romans, a practice which perhaps still persists in parts of France. The wood, also, has been highly esteemed through the ages, being especially sought after in ship-building and for use for piles, fence-posts and other purposes where durability in contact with water is desired.

The affection with which the English people regard this Elm is well indicated in the familiar lines in Browning's "Home Thoughts from Abroad:"

"Oh! to be in England, now that April's there!
Whoever wakes in England sees some morning, unaware,
That the lowest boughs and the brushwood sheaf
Round the elm tree bole are in tiny leaf."

THE SCOTCH ELM OR WITCH ELM

THE Scotch Elm, Dutch Elm, Mountain or Witch Elm, is said to be the most beaut-tiful of all the European species of Elms. As will be seen from the pictures on the plate, it is very distinctive in its habit of growth and the characters of its foliage and fruit. The leafless tree has a most attractive symmetry, while the yellow green leaves with their evenly serrate margins are of a beautiful form. They are generally larger than the leaves of the English Elm, and hang down more heavily. The fruit is especially notable for the curious beak-like hooks on the outer ends.

The history of this Elm in Europe, especially in the British Isles, where it is thought to be the native species, abounds in traditions of those early times when witches and evil spirits were taken seriously into account by mankind. It is said to have been commonly planted in such a position that its shade should fall upon the lich-gate of the church-yard. The twigs of it were believed to be potent in hastening the coming of the butter in the churn. Decoctions of the blossoms and the inner bark were largely used as medicine.

Like the other Elms, this species after a hundred years attains a great height and large diameter. In Gilbert White's "Selborne" a record is made of a large tree partially blown down in 1703, which measured eight feet in diameter and furnished eight loads of timber. Some specimens are believed to live for several centuries before they die of old age. The large trees are generally less tall and more spreading than English Elms of similar age.

This Elm seems to have been planted in America only to a very slight extent. It might well receive more attention in this respect in order that its unique beauty might become more generally known, and that there be greater variety in the trees of our parks and private grounds.

Both the English Elm and the Scotch Elm have been developed into a large num-ber of horticultural varieties. In the case of the latter species some of the more important of these forms are: The Purple-leaved Elm (variety *atropurpurea*); the Fastigiate Elm (variety *fastigiata*); the Camperdown or Weeping Elm (variety *Camperdowni*); the Dwarf Elm (variety *nana*); the Tricuspid Elm, with three-lobed leaves (variety *tricus-pis*). Several varieties vary in the shape or color of the leaves, some being yellow, others purple when young and green when mature, while others are very dark green.

SCOTCH ELM — WITCH ELM
ULMUS MONTANA

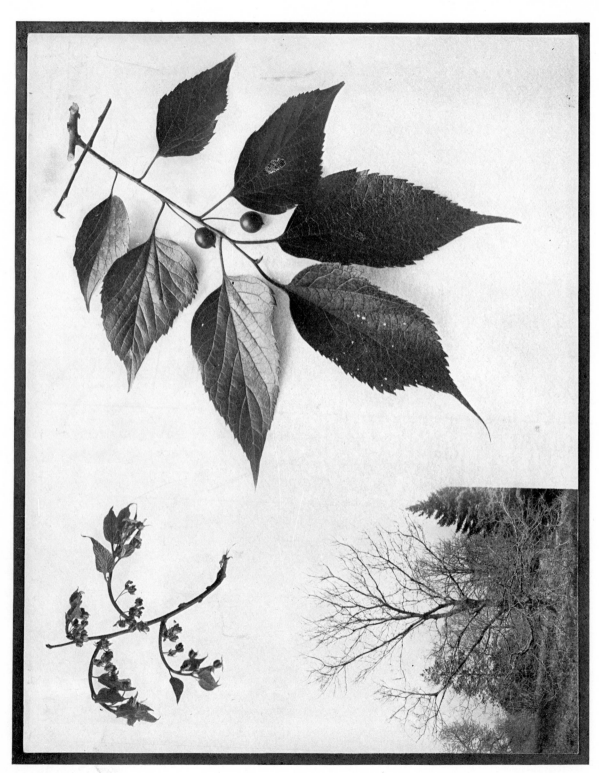

HACKBERRY — SUGARBERRY
CELTIS OCCIDENTALIS

THE HACKBERRY OR SUGARBERRY

THE Hackberry is a tree with a very wide range, and with great variations in the different parts of its range. It is found as a native from Massachusetts, Ontario, and Nebraska, south to Florida, Missouri, and Texas, and occasionally even west of the Rocky Mountains, although in the latter region it is generally a shrubby tree of quite different appearance. In the lower parts of the Mississippi Valley it attains a size and dignity comparable to that of the American Elm, reaching a height of more than a hundred feet and a trunk diameter of two or three feet. The species belongs to the Elm family, and in these magnificent trees the relationship is readily credited. In most regions, however, the Hackberry is more likely to be found as a much smaller tree, or even as a shrub, and the presence of purplish berry-like fruits, as well as the very irregular character of the branches, give a very different appearance from that given by the Elms. The small greenish flowers appear in May upon the young shoots when the leaves are just beginning to develop, the condition being well shown in the upper left-hand picture of the plate. The pollen-bearing and the seed-bearing flowers are generally separated, the former being borne in clusters along the base of the young shoots, while the latter are borne singly in the axils of the young leaves. In due time each of the latter develops into a long-stemmed berry, two of which are shown in the right-hand picture of the plate. The slender, pointed leaves with their beautiful serrated margins are generally larger on one side than on the other, a condition suggestive of the leaves of the Elm.

The Hackberry trees are rather decorative at almost any season of the year, and may occasionally be planted in parks and ornamental grounds to decided advantage. They are hardy in the Northern States but are likely to be erratic in their growth, so that they serve better for planting singly or in small, irregular groups than for planting in rows where a uniform growth is desired. The picturesque appearance of the tree in winter is shown in the specimen illustrated on the plate. The trunks and larger branches often have a characteristic warty bark which is very likely to attract attention.

The Hackberry is not very often planted for shade or ornament in the Eastern States, though it thrives well there and is of interest on account of its habit of growth and comparative rarity. It is especially valuable however in the partially arid regions of the West where its great ability to withstand drouth renders it one of the few trees that can be grown at all. The young trees are readily raised from seeds.

THE RED MULBERRY

THE Red Mulberry is the only native Mulberry in the eastern United States. It is distributed from southern New England west to Ontario, Michigan, and Nebraska, and south to Texas and Florida. In the northern parts of its range it is a small tree, rarely reaching a height greater than twenty-five feet, but in the valleys of the Ohio and Mississippi Rivers it becomes much larger, even reaching a height of sixty or seventy feet. Throughout its range it is often planted either as an ornamental tree or to furnish food for birds or poultry.

The general characteristics of the species are well shown on the plate. In summer it is easily recognized by the large, rounded leaves, suggestive of those of the Linden in their outlines but very different in their texture, the Mulberry leaves having the veins, as seen on the upper surface, sunken into the blade in a most characteristic fashion. Many of the leaves are lobed in a way suggestive of the lobing on the leaves of the Japanese Mulberry. Professor L. H. Bailey suggests that this "affords another of those interesting parallelisms which exist between the Japanese and eastern American floras." The blossoms appear in spring when the leaves are partially developed, the pollen-bearing and the seed-bearing being in separate catkins upon the same or upon different trees. The former fall off after shedding the pollen, while the latter gradually develop into the interesting fruit which ripens during July or August, turning to a dark reddish purple color, the berries being edible and eagerly sought by many birds.

This tree has many qualities which have been utilized by man. In addition to the uses of the fruit already mentioned, it is valued in some parts of the South for fattening hogs and an unsuccessful attempt has been made to utilize the leaves for feeding silkworms. The Choctaw Indians formerly made a kind of coarse cloth from the inner bark, after macerating it in hot water and ashes. The wood is very hard and durable and has been utilized for fence-posts and in ship-building, being an especial favorite for the latter purpose.

In Texas there is a variety named *tomentosa* notable for the whitish pubescence on the under surface of the leaves. The Lampasas Mulberry is a form of this selected for its large fruit.

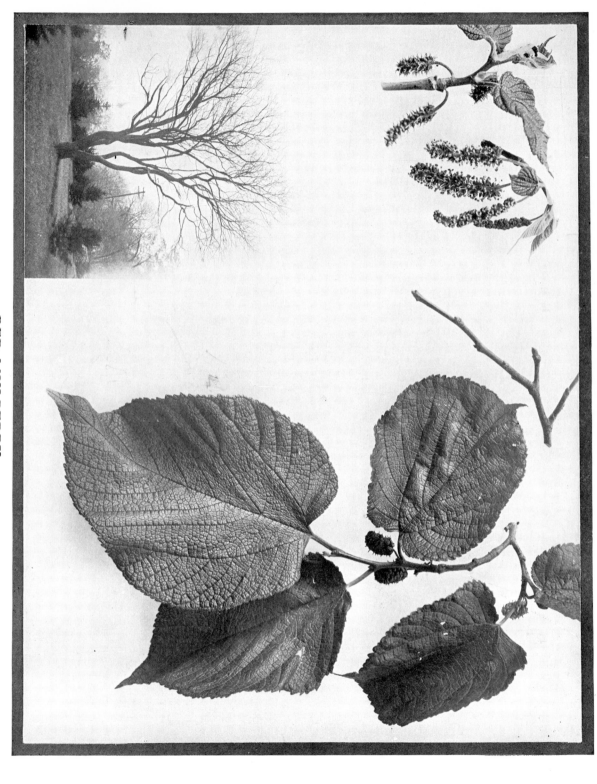

WHITE MULBERRY

MORUS ALBA

THE WHITE MULBERRY

PERHAPS the most interesting thing about the White Mulberry is the fact that from time immemorial the leaves of this tree have been fed to silkworms in China, whence it was introduced early in the Seventeenth Century into England. The species is at once distinguished from the Red Mulberry in summer by its smaller, much smoother and more shining leaves with obtuse or rounded tips, as well as by the white fruits. It has been very generally planted as an ornamental tree, and occasionally appears to have sprung up spontaneously, perhaps from the seeds scattered by birds.

As may be seen from the specimen pictured on the plate, a leafless Mulberry tree of good size bears a striking resemblance to a neglected Apple tree, the manner of growth of the trunk and larger branches being very similar. The species is hardy as far north as Southern New England and Northern Ohio, and has been extensively planted for its fruit as well as for its leaves.

As is so generally the case with trees which have been long in cultivation, there are several distinct varieties of the White Mulberry. The Black Mulberry is another species which is a native of Persia, and has been very generally cultivated in England and other European countries, but seems to have received very little attention in America except in California and the South; while during recent years the hardy Russian Mulberry has been very extensively advertised and widely planted in the more northern regions, where the other species cannot withstand the climate. The Russian Mulberry is of especial value in planting to encourage the presence of birds, and to furnish them with a food which will help to protect cultivated cherries and other fruits. It is now considered a variety (*Tatarica*) of the White Mulberry.

One of the most fascinating chapters in the annals of horticulture has been published by Professor Bailey under the title: "The Strange History of the Mulberries" in the volume on The Evolution of Our Native Fruits. As a result of long study of literature and specimens he classifies the mulberries grown in America as follows: White Mulberry (*Morus alba*) with two distinct varieties: *Tatarica* or Russian Mulberry, and *nervosa*, as well as several named horticultural forms; Japanese Mulberry (*M. Japonica*) a recently introduced species; Multicaulis Mulberry (*M. Multicaulis*); a species which in China is the chief source of silkworm food and which by other authorities has generally been considered a variety of the White Mulberry; Black Mulberry (*M. nigra*); Native Red Mulberry (*M. rubra*) and a small southwestern species, *M. celtidifolia*.

THE OSAGE ORANGE OR BOW-WOOD

FROM several points of view the Osage Orange is a tree of extraordinary interest The historian will tell you that long before the settlement of America by the whites, the Indians used the wood for war-clubs and bows, a custom that gave rise to one of its common names—Bow-wood—and that its other common name is due to the fact that it was introduced into cultivation among the earliest settlers in St. Louis by specimens procured from the Osage Indians. He will add that during the development of the great prairie region beyond the Mississippi the species served an important purpose as a hedge plant, thousands of farmers utilizing it for fencing their fields, although the introduction of improved wire-fencing materials has rendered such hedges of comparatively little importance to-day. But these old hedges now furnish fence-posts of extraordinary value.

The botanist will tell you that the Osage Orange is of interest from root to fruit. The bark of the roots is of a bright orange color and furnishes a yellow dye; the ridged and scaly bark of the trunk furnishes tannin for making leather; the branches have attractive leaves with curious thorns at their bases; the pollen-bearing and seed-bearing flowers are borne upon separate trees, the former, as may be seen on the upper twig shown in the plate, being in abundant clusters, and the latter, as may be seen in the lower twig, being in round heads. Each of these round heads matures into one of the strangest fruits known to science: the so-called "orange" is a greenish compound fruit made up of a large number of seed-bearing fruits grown together on their edges.

The landscape gardener will tell you that the Osage Orange is of especial interest because it is hardy at the North, although its native home is in the region of the old Indian Territory, and because of its ease of propagation and the variety of uses to which it can be put. It grows readily from green wood cuttings and serves admirably for hedges as well as for single planting, making in the latter case a bushy tree which when loaded with fruit is sure to attract general attention. It has also the great advantage of comparative freedom from attack by insect and fungus enemies.

In its original region the Osage Orange sometimes reaches a height of sixty feet and a trunk diameter of three feet. It grows especially along the river bottoms in parts of Arkansas, the old Indian Territory and Texas.

OSAGE ORANGE — BOW-WOOD

TOXYLON POMIFERUM

SWAMP MAGNOLIA — SWEET BAY
MAGNOLIA GLAUCA

MAGNOLIA FAMILY

THE SWAMP MAGNOLIA OR SWEET BAY

MOST of the Magnolias are Southern forms finding a congenial home in the climate of our Southern states. The present species, however, is of especial interest because it apparently has long been growing naturally as far north as Massachusetts, a famous station for it occurring near Gloucester, although practically all the plants in the colony have now disappeared through the greed of collectors. From Long Island to Florida the species is found in swampy places, a deciduous shrub in the North, an evergreen tree in the South, but everywhere notable for the beauty of its leaves, flowers and fruit. It is native to the coast region, and on our southern border extends west to Texas. The largest and finest trees in Florida reach a height of sixty or seventy feet and a trunk diameter of two or more feet. The small, creamy-white fragrant flowers, the hairy leaf-buds, the glossy dark-green leaves, and the smooth, shining, red fruits are the most characteristic features of the Swamp Magnolia. It is readily distinguished from any other native species, although there is a shrubby Chinese form, *Magnolia pumila*, frequently planted in the South, which is quite similar to it.

A special interest attaches to the Massachusetts colony of this Magnolia: it gave the name to one of the most popular summer resorts along the coast; it furnished plants for many of the gardens in New England; and it served as the inspiration of those beautiful lines by Whittier:

> "Long they sat and talked together,
> Of the marvellous valley hidden in the depths of Gloucester woods,
> Full of plants that love the summer, blooms of warmer latitudes,
> Where the Artic birch is braided by the tropics' flowery vines,
> And the white magnolia blossoms star the twilight of the pines."

In a rare book upon "The Trees of Salem," John Robinson, a well-known Massachusetts botanist, wrote in 1891: "It is said that Dr. Manasseh Cutler, of Hamilton, first called attention to the Sweet Magnolia in Gloucester, near where the present popular summer resort perpetuates the name and fame of the most northerly station of this plant. Its fragrant blossoms attracted him to the spot, and ever since it has been eagerly sought for its flowers and for transplanting into gardens. . . . . Why the Magnolia should be found in Gloucester is a mystery. 'The Hermit,' a well-known Gloucester character, a student and lover of nature, feels sure that it was brought from the South and planted in some old garden. By changes in the location of the settlement it was lost sight of, and the woods growing up in the region of the deserted dwelling-places the plants were left to themselves and increased." On the other hand, it seems equally probable that the colony was started by seeds dropped by birds.

The Swamp Magnolia is justly a favorite for ornamental planting; it is hardy, and beautiful, and native to America. A long-leaved variety has been developed which is even more desirable than the type, as it continues in blossom for a longer period.

THE MOUNTAIN MAGNOLIA OR CUCUMBER TREE

THE Cucumber Tree derives its common name from the curious fruit, which when green is very suggestive of a cucumber. The tree is also called the Mountain Magnolia, being a typical representative of the Magnolia family, and growing in abundance upon the mountain sides. It is a Southern species, ranging from Ontario and New York to Alabama, Kentucky, and Mississippi. The species is hardy further north than the region to which it is indigenous, and is often utilized for ornamental planting in New York and other States.

When growing in the open, the Cucumber Tree assumes the conical form shown in the noble specimen pictured on the plate. As will be noticed, the lower branches sweep the ground and the general outline of the massive foliage has great beauty as seen against the horizon. Although the leaves are large, their shining green color and abundance on the branches give the tree a most pleasing effect. When growing in the forests of the mountain valleys of the Carolinas, where the crowding together has compelled each tree to shoot upward in order to get light and air, the trunks rise as massive columns bare of twigs or branches for thirty or forty feet before spreading out into the head. The flowers appear in late spring or early summer, being of a yellow or greenish-yellow color, and of a form suggestive of the blossoms of the nearly related Tulip Tree. After the petals have fallen the gradual development of the curious fruit takes place, these changing to a dark red color as they ripen, and casting out the large berries in the interesting fashion pictured on the plate. These berries hang on threads for a longer or shorter time until finally they are eaten by various birds, by means of which the black seeds inside are scattered to new localities.

The chief objection to this tree for ornamental planting is that it has a tendency to drop the leaves more or less through the summer. This objection may be obviated by planting the variety named *cordata* by Professor Sargent because the leaves are often heart-shaped at the base. This variety has been cultivated as an ornamental tree for many years, its leaves being broader and darker green, and less liable to fall off than those of the typical Cucumber Tree. Its flowers also are smaller and of a brighter yellow color, so that it has decided advantages for use in landscape planting.

MOUNTAIN MAGNOLIA — CUCUMBER TREE
MAGNOLIA ACUMINATA

UMBRELLA TREE
MAGNOLIA TRIPETALA

THE UMBRELLA TREE

THE Umbrella Tree is one of the most distinctive of the native Magnolias: the large leaves are clustered at the ends of the branches and are commonly a foot or more long; they arise from smooth hairless buds and branches, appearing in advance of the large, malodorous flowers, which have three characteristic light green petal-like sepals protecting the flower. These sepals probably gave the common name Umbrella Tree to the species, as well as led the great Swedish botanist Linné to give it its technical name, *tripetala*. Examples of the large glabrous buds and the interesting fruits are well shown on the plate.

The Umbrella Tree is one of those widely distributed species which may be found in many places, but seldom in great abundance. It is especially at home on the slopes of the Appalachian Mountains, and also occurs in many of the Southern States. It is a favorite tree for ornamental planting, good examples reaching a height of forty feet and having a massive effect due to the clusters of large leaves held on the ends of the branches.

Another tree that should be mentioned in this connection is the Laurel Magnolia or True Magnolia or Bull Bay, the species called *M. grandiflora* by Linnæus and *M. fœtida* by Professor Sargent, who says it is "the most splendid ornamental tree in the American forest." Native to our own Southland, this species has been largely planted by landscape gardeners throughout the temperate climates of the world, its appeal to admiration being based on its large size, its beautiful leaves and flowers, and the numerous varieties which European horticulturists have developed.

There are many imported kinds of Magnolias now in cultivation. Most of these are from China or other Asiatic countries while some of the most beautiful are hybrids. In planting any of the Magnolias it is desirable to get well-grown nursery stock and to transplant in spring as the buds are starting to grow. Most sorts thrive best in a well drained loamy soil, though the Swamp Magnolia will thrive in a wetter situation. For ornamental use as specimen plants for early blossoming, this group of trees and shrubs is unrivalled.

THE TULIP TREE

THE Tulip Tree is known either as a shade tree or a timber tree throughout a large part of eastern America. For the former purpose it is deservedly a favorite, having a symmetrical habit of growth, an extraordinary beauty of blossom and foliage, and great freedom from attack by insect and fungus enemies. It also grows rapidly when successfully transplanted, doing best in a moist, loamy soil.

The winter-buds of the Tulip Tree are interesting and characteristic. The two large brown scales envelop the tiny leaves, the outer of which are fully formed within the scales. Sir John Lubbock has shown that the curious shape of the leaf is an adaptation to the manner of folding within the bud. As the leaf develops the scales act as stipules, their bases encircling the twig. At first the foliage is light yellowish green, becoming somewhat darker as the leaves attain full size.

The blossoms of the Tulip Tree are beautiful and interesting. They appear early in summer, in the more northern states usually in June. Each flower in its outline is very suggestive of that of the tulip, being held erect on the end of the twig in a most character istic fashion. The flowers are freely visited by insects.

In the great river valleys of the Ohio and the Mississippi the Tulip Tree is one of the most valuable timber trees, commonly attaining a great size and height. It is often called Whitewood and in many localities Yellow Poplar, although the latter seems an unfortunate name. In young trees the bark is quite smooth and of an ash gray color, while in older trees it becomes much darker and rougher.

At least three horticultural varieties of the Tulip Tree have already been introduced. In one of these the lobes of the leaf are wanting, which is certainly a doubtful improvement, for the beauty of the leaf of the normal form lies very largely in its distinctive lobing. In another variety the foliage is variegated, also a somewhat doubtful improvement, for the uniform coloring of the leaves of the tree, whether in the greenness of summer or the mellow yellowness of autumn, is another of its attractions. The third variety has upright branches, suggestive of those of the Lombardy Popular. Never having seen this form I can only suggest that it seems of doubtful utility for general planting.

TULIP TREE
L. RIODENDRON TULIPIFERA

PAPAW

ASIMINA TRILOBA

THE PAPAW

THE curious fruit of the Papaw is probably familiar to more people than even the strange fruit of the Persimmon, because the Papaw has a more northward range. It occurs from New Jersey west to Michigan and Nebraska, and is especially abundant in the great Mississippi Valley region, where it often forms the prevailing vegetation of the underwoods. For the Papaw is essentially a shade-loving species, its large tropical-looking leaves clustered toward the ends of the branches enabling it to build up materials of growth in comparatively subdued light. In consequence of thus living beneath other trees, it is commonly of a shrub-like form, though under favorable conditions it may become a spreading tree with a height of forty feet and a trunk diameter of ten or twelve inches. It especially occurs in the moist, rich soil of river valleys, where it often grows into dense thickets.

The blossom of the Papaw is as curious as its fruit. One who is familiar with the flower of the little plant called Wild Ginger can readily get an idea of the Papaw blossom by imagining the latter considerably magnified. The Papaw blossoms are ill-smelling and have a diameter of about two inches, with three hairy, greenish sepals, with six more or less hairy wine-red petals arranged in two rows, the inner row nectar-bearing. These flowers appear in April as the leaves develop, and the fruit matures in autumn. This fruit is suggestive of the tropical Papaw, to which fact its common name is due. It is shaped something like a short banana, and contains inside the green outer skin a soft yellow flesh in which the flat wrinkled seeds are imbedded. The sweetish-pungent taste, with the somewhat disagreeable odor, is not attractive to most people, although apparently a liking for it may be acquired if one begins young enough.

The Pond Apple (*Anona glabra*) is another member of the tropical Custard Apple family which occurs as far north as Florida and the Bahama Islands. The largest specimens reach a height of forty feet and a trunk diameter of eighteen inches. The fruit is much the size and shape of a long apple, but is not much prized for eating.

The tropical Papaw from which the name of our tree is derived is often called the Melon Papaw (*Caraca Papaya*). It reaches the United States in Southern Florida where its general resemblance to one of the palms is often noted. The leaves are clustered at the top of the trunk and the large fruits are borne just below them.

THE SASSAFRAS

IN the consciousness of one whose youth was passed in a region where the Sassafras was abundant this species is sure to occupy a unique position. The peculiar aromatic taste of the bark and root, and the accompanying rather pleasing aromatic odor, serve to set the Sassafras apart from all the other trees of the forest. As if to emphasize this fact, the leaves take on three forms, each of which is distinctive. In the oval form, which perhaps is the commonest on most trees, the margin is entire and symmetrical. In the mitten form the margin has one large thumb-like projection that gives the leaf its distinctive shape. Sometimes there are two such lobes, and all three forms may be found side by side upon the same twig.

The flowers of the Sassafras appear in May, generally a little in advance of the leaves. They are of a greenish-yellow color which is not very conspicuous, and are borne in corymb-like racemes on the ends of the twigs. The pollen-bearing and the seed-bearing blossoms are usually upon separate trees. There are no petals, but the sepals are somewhat petal-like and give the individual flower an expanse of about half an inch. An interesting part of their structure is found in the arrangement of the straight stamens in three series, and the presence at the base of each of the filaments of the inner three stamens of a pair of stalked glands, presumably for the secretion of nectar. These blossoms develop during the latter part of summer into blue, oblong drupes about half an inch in length.

The fact that the Sassafras has long been esteemed as a medicine is shown by the statement, in George B. Emerson's "Trees and Shrubs of Massachusetts," that its roots formed part of the first cargo exported from that State. At present it is not so highly esteemed for its medicinal properties as it was in former days, but it still is largely used, especially as a flavoring for various medicines.

Throughout most of its range, which includes the region east of Kansas and Texas, north to New Hampshire and Michigan, the Sassafras is usually a shrub or small tree, occasionally, however, in the Southwest reaching a great size. Trees of a height of one hundred feet and a diameter of six or seven feet give one a very different impression of the possibilities of the species from that which one gets from the small trees of the New England region. The bark of the shrubs and quite young trees is of a characteristic greenish-gray color, and is commonly marked with even striations. When the trees reach a diameter of several inches the bark of the trunk becomes firmly ridged with many rather deep vertical furrows. Its color is dark reddish brown.

SWEET GUM — BILSTED

THE SWEET GUM OR BILSTED

THE Sweet Gum or Liquidambar is a tree of extraordinary interest for several reasons. It has resinous foliage of a most distinctive shape, it has picturesque fruits on long stems, it has curious corky wings upon the branches, and it is a survivor of a very ancient geologic type. It is essentially a Southern species, chiefly inhabiting lowlands and often occupying large areas which are inundated during much of the year. It occurs as far north as Connecticut, and reaches an immense size in the lower valley of the Mississippi River. It is called by three distinctive names—Sweet Gum, Liquidambar, and Bilsted. At first glance the leaves of this tree remind one of some of the Maples, but their lobes are much more regular, and the posterior lobes are larger and more distinctive than those of any of the Maples. In summer the upper surface of these leaves is of a lustrous bright green color, while its autumn coloring has been well described by Miss Keeler in these words: "The autumnal coloring is not simply a flame, it is a conflagration; in reds and yellows it equals the Maples, and in addition it has the dark purples and smoky browns of the Ash."

The blossoms appear in May on the ends of the new twigs, the pollen-bearing flowers being held in long catkins, while the seed-bearing ones are in heads on the ends of rather long twigs. The former fall off after the pollen is shed, while the latter gradually develop into the curious fruits that suggest the fruiting balls of the Sycamore or Buttonwood tree, although they have not the solid surface of the latter fruits.

The Liquidambar is hardy as far north as southern New England and wherever it may be grown successfully it is exceedingly desirable as an ornamental tree, especially on account of the distinctive beauty of its autumn foliage. Mr. Warren H. Manning, a well-known horticulturist, writes that along the northern limits of its range the Sweet Gum trees may be protected for a few years until they become established so they will be able to endure the climate and grow to a fair size. This species is especially popular in England on account of its autumnal coloring.

The name Liquidambar is derived from the curious gum called commercially "Copalm balm" which is produced by the sap when the bark is injured. Centuries ago this gum was known as "liquid amber" and the great botanist Linnæus gave the name Liquidambar to this and related trees. A similar product from Oriental trees is used to burn as incense.

THE WITCH HAZEL

AS the Alder is the first tree to come upon the stage in spring, expressing the prologue of the play of the changing seasons, so the Witch Hazel is the last to show itself and close the play with a fitting epilogue. It not only expresses the complete fruition of the season by means of its exploding fruits, but it also leaves in the spectator's mind a promise of blossoms for another season by means of the slender, strap-like petals of its yellow flowers. Everyone who has wandered in autumn along hillsides or woodsy byroads where the Witch Hazel grows will agree with Thoreau that it "is always pleasant to come upon it unexpectedly as you are threading the woods in such places."

The Witch Hazel is more likely to be found in the form of a shrub than of a tree, although it occasionally assumes the latter condition, especially in mountainous regions. It is widely distributed in eastern America, and the characteristic form of the leaves and fruits is well shown on the upper part of the accompanying plate. The bark of the lower part of the trunk is generally smooth or slightly scaly, while the inner bark is of a curious reddish-purple color. The wood is hard and heavy, weighing forty-two pounds per cubic foot. The winter-buds are slender and pointed and commonly bent toward the tip in a characteristic fashion, as may be seen on the end of the upper twig in the plate. The hard, woody fruits have two cells, in each of which there is a little nut which is shot out several feet in autumn when the fruits explode. Many people no doubt have had experiences like that so delightfully described by the late William Hamilton Gibson in *Sharp Eyes*: "I had been attracted by a bush which showed an unusual profusion of bloom, and while standing close beside it in admiration I was suddenly stung on the cheek by some missile, and the next instant shot in the eye by another, the mysterious marksman having apparently let off both barrels of his little gun directly in my face."

The New England poets have very frequently referred to the Witch Hazel in their writings, one of the happiest of these references being found in the familiar verse by Whittier·

> "Through the gray and sombre wood,
>   Against the dusk of fir and pine,
> Last of their floral sisterhood,
>   The Hazel's yellow blossoms shine."

WITCH HAZEL
HAMAMELIS VIRGINIANA

SYCAMORE — BUTTONWOOD

PLATANUS OCCIDENTALIS

THE SYCAMORE OR BUTTONWOOD

I T is fitting that so distinctive a tree as the Buttonwood, or American Plane-tree which in many places is more commonly called the Sycamore, should be the only representative of its family in our region. It has many characteristics that help to give it a unique place in one's consciousness, and one who has been familiar with it as it grows to magnificent proportions along the banks of the Mississippi and Ohio rivers and their tributaries would always wish to see it in that situation described by the poet Bryant.

> "Clear are the depths where its eddies play,
> And dimples deepen and whirl away;
> And the plane tree's speckled arms o'er-shoot
> The swifter current that mines its root."

As seen at a distance the most characteristic feature of the Buttonwood is the peculiar color of the bark on the trunk. Great white blotches stand out most markedly, covered here and there by large flecks of brown bark. The branches also have a characteristic brush-like manner of growth that is easily recognized from afar. As one draws nearer to the tree the distinctive characters of the almost circular, palmately-lobed leaves may be seen. These leaves are lighter below than above, the under surface being covered with a cottony down which is especially marked along the principal veins. The base of the petiole covers the bud in a most interesting and characteristic fashion. When the leaves appear in spring they are accompanied by large stipules that usually drop off when the foliage attains full size.

The flowers of the Sycamore appear early in May, about the time the leaves begin to develop. The pollen-bearing and the seed-bearing blossoms are separate but often upon the same branch, being massed together in small round heads with rather short hairy stalks. The tree apparently depends upon cross-pollination by the wind, the seed-bearing flowers on a given tree maturing in advance of the pollen-bearing ones.

The fruit ripens in autumn into round balls that give the name Buttonwood to the tree, these balls breaking up through the winter and the seeds are scattered far and wide by wind and water. The range of the Buttonwood extends from New England west to Nebraska and south to Texas and Florida. The trees often attain an enormous size, and seem to reach their largest proportions in the valleys of the Ohio and Mississippi Rivers.

In the extreme West and Southwest two other species of Sycamore are found. One of these, known technically as *Platanus racemosa*, becomes a large tree and is found abundantly in Southern California. The other, *Platanus Wrightii*, does not attain so great a size but is found abundantly in the mountainous regions of Arizona and New Mexico.

THE MOUNTAIN ASH

THE American Mountain Ash is much less commonly planted as an ornamental tree than is the European species. It grows spontaneously along river banks, and in other moist situations, over a wide range extending from Newfoundland to Manitoba on the north, south to Minnesota and Michigan, and along the mountainous elevations to North Carolina. It is distinctly a Northern species, seeming to thrive best on the colder slopes of the mountains or in the shaded swamps to the southward. It commonly reaches a height of about twenty feet and a trunk diameter of one foot, and is an attractive tree either in blossom or in fruit. The large clusters of small white flowers are well shown in the plate. They develop late in spring or early in summer, just after the compound leaves have reached their full size, and are gradually succeeded by the small round fruit which becomes bright red when it ripens in autumn and often remains upon the tree during the winter months.

This Mountain Ash is an extremely variable species. Many of the tree books discuss the Elder-leaved Mountain Ash, under the name *Sorbus sambucifolia*, as a distinct form, but admit that its claim to distinction is of doubtful value. Professor Sargent, in his authoritative "Manual of The Trees of North America," treats of this as a variety, *decora*, which he says is apparently connected with the typical species by many intermediate forms. This variety is a Northern form, extending south to Minnesota and the mountains of Northern New York and Northern New England. It is often cultivated for ornamental purposes in Canada. In the Cyclopedia of Horticulture the name *sambucifolia* is given standing as a species.

The typical form of the American Mountain Ash seems to be less desirable for landscape planting than the European species, which is more readily obtained and gives a more decorative effect. The variety *decora* however is an especially beautiful tree when loaded with fruit.

There are two shrubby species of Sorbus which are called Chokeberries: the Red Chokeberry (*S. arbutifolia*) is widely distributed east of Minnesota and Louisiana; it reaches a height of ten or twelve feet and bears small reddish berries. The Black Chokeberry (*S. melanocarpa*) is generally a smaller shrub with slightly larger shining black berries.

MOUNTAIN ASH

EUROPEAN MOUNTAIN ASH

THE EUROPEAN MOUNTAIN ASH

VERY few trees have been so widely and extensively planted for ornamental purposes in America as the European Mountain Ash. It has many advantages for this purpose, being easily obtained from all nurserymen and bearing beautiful flowers in spring, decorative foliage in summer, and brilliantly colored, attractive fruit in autumn and winter. It grows fairly rapidly, and is hardy throughout the Northern States. The general character of the leaves, stems and fruit, as well as the habit of growth of a large tree. are shown on the plate.

Like so many trees that have long been planted about the abodes of man in Europe, this Mountain Ash has many traditions associated with it. In parts of Scotland it is called the "Witchin tree," it having long been supposed that the branches of this tree were potent against the spells of witches. It is also very generally known as the Rowan tree, which is sometimes contracted to the Roan tree, and under this name it was credited with similar potency. An old English verse runs:

"The spells were vain and the boys returned
To the queen in sorrowful mood,
Crying that witches have no power
Where there is roan tree wood."

In some districts in Scotland it is said to have been formerly the custom to have sheep and lambs on May day jump through a hoop made of the branches of the Rowan tree in order that the flock might prosper through the summer. Mrs. Dyson writes: "It is the Rowan or Roan tree—that is, the Whispering tree; the tree that knows the secret spells and charms; the tree of the witches or, as it is sometimes called, the Witchin or Wiggin tree." These names seem not at all to have been used in America in connection with this or our native species of Mountain Ash. Still another name of this tree in England was the Service tree, due to the fact that the fruit was used in making a kind of beer called by the Latin term Cerevisia, which was contracted into the English word Service.

There are several distinct varieties of the European Mountain Ash. One of these called *dulcis* is very hardy and bears fruit which is said to be desirable for preserves; another called *fastigiata* sends its branches up in a pyramidal form; another called *pendula* is given a weeping effect by its drooping twigs; other varieties have yellow fruits and still others have variegated foliage.

THE CANADA JUNEBERRY OR SHADBUSH

THE observer who should follow the trees through the year, to note the distinctive effect which each kind gives to the landscape, would find that many of them occupy the most conspicuous position during some brief period. This may be due to a variety of causes: in the lengthening catkins of the Alder it is as the first token of yielding winter that the species stands apart from all others; in the beautiful branches of the Pussy Willow it is the display of brilliant blossoms upon a sombre background; in the flowers and fruits of the Red Maple it is the lighting up of the landscape by glorious hues of red; in the case of the Juneberry or Shadbush the effect is due to the brilliant white petals held in clustered masses in the foreground against a changing background of the grays and greens of the developing foliage. These flowers are borne in racemes, there being generally five or more in a cluster and each flower having its parts arranged in groups of five. The blossoms have a sweetish odor which, together with the nectar that they secrete, attracts great numbers of bees and other insects to carry the pollen from tree to tree. The young leaves have their upper surfaces folded together, and are sparsely covered with whitish hairs which drop off as the leaf reaches maturity. The fruit matures a few weeks after the petals have fallen, its general characters being well shown in the accompanying plate. When ripe it is generally reddish or reddish purple and the meagre pulp has a slightly sweetish taste.

The Canada Juneberry is often called the Shadbush, although there are also other species, which are not so likely to assume the tree form, to which this name is given. It grows commonly as a shrub or small tree over a great range, extending from Newfoundland to Lake Superior on the north, to Minnesota and Kansas on the west, and to Louisiana and Florida on the south. It is especially likely to be found in sparse woods and along the margins of streams flowing down hillsides, although is not usually found in very wet situations. The bark of the trunk is of a characteristic greenish-gray color and generally is quite smooth. The buds are small and pointed and the bark of the youngest branches is of a brownish or purplish-red color.

The Juneberry is of special value for ornamental planting on account of the beauty of its blossoms in early spring. It is hardy and will thrive in partial shade, so that it may be planted to advantage along the borders of small groves of other trees.

CANADA JUNEBERRY — SHADBUSH
AMELANCHIER CANADENSIS

DWARF JUNEBERRY — SHADBUSH
AMELANCHIER OBOVALIS

THE DWARF JUNEBERRY OR SHADBUSH

ALTHOUGH there has been some difference of opinion among students of trees as as to whether the Dwarf Juneberry should take rank as a distinct species or not, it is readily distinguished by anyone in spring and summer. When the leaves and blossoms are developing the growing parts are covered with a dense coating of short white hairs that serves to identify it at once. Later this hairy coating is largely lost, but the form may then be known by the leaves, which are longer and more slender than those of the Canada Juneberry. The petals of the flowers are short and broad in the Dwarf species, and long and narrow in the Canada species. The former commonly occurs as a low shrub along the borders of marshes and streams over a very large part of the United States, from Minnesota eastward. In many localities along the coast it is called the Shadbush, because it blossoms at the time the shad come up the rivers, while in interior regions it is called the Swamp Sugar Pear, because of the sweetness of the red fruits that ripen early in summer.

In the western regions of North America the Alder-leaved Service-berry (*Amelanchier alnifolia*) seems to take the place of the Eastern forms. This is readily known by its characteristic leaves, which are short and broad and distinctly serrate on the terminal half of the margin. It extends northward to the Yukon River and eastward to Michigan. Its fruits, instead of being red like the Juneberries, are bluish black with more or less of a glaucous bloom. These fruits have long been highly valued by the Indians, who dry them for food.

The especial value of the various species of Shadbush from the point of view of the landscape gardener lies in the beauty of their blossoms in early spring. They can be used to light up a landscape picture at a time when they are especially welcome, and one form or another may be utilized in almost any sort of soil and to produce its effect at almost any height.

During recent years botanists have classified certain other shrubby forms of native Shadbushes as distinct species; and one species from Europe and another from Asia have been introduced for landscape use. The former is the European Service Berry (*Amelanchier vulgaris*): it is a low shrub with short racemes of white flowers which are succeeded by blue-black fruits. The latter (*Amelanchier Asiatica*) is a small tree from China and Japan with its flowers arranged in compound racemes

THE HAWTHORN

THERE is much uncertainty among botanists in regard to the specific standing of our various sorts of Thorn Apples or Hawthorns. Fortunately this uncertainty does not prevent the public from enjoying the beauty of the delicate blossoms in May, when the clusters of white flowers are revealed against the background of the young leaves, the attractiveness of the clean green foliage during the weeks of summer, or the striking display of the scarlet haws in autumn. Even in winter the closely interlacing branches with their long decorative spines furnish a sight meriting careful attention.

On the inside of the blossom there is a large, greenish, saucer-like surface on which nectar is secreted. This nectar, together with the delicate odor which advertises its presence, serves to attract to the flowers a great variety of bees and other insects, which bring about cross-pollination.

As is well known, the European Hawthorn is a favorite shrub for hedges in England, where its beauty has been repeatedly celebrated by the masters of English literature. The native trees are occasionally used in America for hedges, but not to any considerable extent. They are very desirable for this purpose, as well as for planting singly or in groups for landscape adornment. They are commonly quite free from insect or fungus attack, are hardy, and are attractive throughout the year. Hundreds of distinct species are now recognized by botanists, but the extraordinary variability of the parts upon which claims for specific distinction are usually based has led to considerable confusion in regard to the precise limits of these various sorts. The pictures upon the plate represent a hitherto unnamed species which has been called *Cratægus Irvingii* by Professor Sargent in honor of Arthur Irving Emerson, who discovered it. It belongs to the Pruinosæ group of species, and has five to ten stamens with rose-colored anthers, and bears red or orange-red fruits. It is found in Massachusetts.

It has been suggested that many of the species of Hawthorn will prove to be natural hybrids of recent occurrence, but Professor Sargent finds no evidence for the theory. The plants produce seed freely and the seedlings show no tendency to variation

HAWTHORN
CRATÆGUS IRVINGII

ENGLISH HAWTHORN

CRATÆGUS OXYACANTHA

THE ENGLISH HAWTHORN

THE literary fame of few trees rests more secure than that of the English Hawthorn, the "May" of the great poets. For centuries the species has been used for hedges and for ornamental planting in Great Britain, and its blossoming beauty has become a part of the mental imagery of every inhabitant. In "Brittannias Pastorals" long ago one of the early poets sang:

> "Mark the faire blooming of the hawthorn-tree,
> Who finely clothed in a robe of white,
> Fill full the wanton eye with May's delight."

And Sir John Mandeville told the story of an old tradition in these words:

"Then was our Lord yled into a gardyn, and there the Jewes scorned hym and made hym a crowne of the branches of the albiespyne, that is whitethorn, which grew in the same gardyn, and setten yt upon hys head. And therefore has the whitethorn many virtues. For he that beareth a branch on hym thereof, no thundre, ne no manre of tempest may dere hym, ne in the house that it is ynne may non evil ghost enter."

A well-known student of English landscapes and English literature, Mr. J. Harvey Bloom, in his "Shakespeare's Garden" says of the Hawthorn: "Its snowy blossoms, massed in profuse luxuriance on their setting of bright green leaves, serve to make a Hawthorn glade one of the loveliest components of English scenery. And when the leaves are painted with their autumnal dyes, and the bright red hips appear, it is almost equally striking." And a modern poet, in *The Century Magazine*, has suggested a beauty of the later season in the lines:

> "Oho, Oho for the hunting,
> In the crisp October morn,
> With the hoar of the frost like a kerchief toss'd
> On the black of the twisted thorn."

The English Hawthorn is known technically as *Cratægus Oxyacantha*. There is one variety of this species which has yellow fruit, but according to Mr. Alfred Rehder's monograph in the "Cyclopedia of Horticulture," most of the many cultivated forms which are commonly referred to *Oxyacantha* really belong to another species, *Cratægus monogyna*. More than a dozen of these garden forms are recognized as distinct; several of these are very attractive, and well worthy of cultivation in parks and private grounds. There are single and double white-flowered varieties, and single and double red-flowered varieties, as well as varieties with pendulous foliage, and others with variegated foliage.

THE BIRD CHERRY OR WILD RED CHERRY

THE Wild Red Cherry, which is also commonly called the Bird Cherry, is one of the most beautiful and distinctive species of the great Rose family. At first sight the young trees remind one of Peach trees, the slender leaves that clothe the long twigs having a very marked resemblance to those of the Peach. These leaves are bright, shining green above and lighter below, while their margins are finely and sharply serrate. During the latter part of summer the trees commonly present a very attractive appearance when the small, globular, brilliant-red cherries are seen against the background of green foliage. These cherries ripen during a long period, and are eaten freely by a great variety of birds although they are so sour that they are not attractive to human taste. Before falling in autumn the leaves commonly turn a distinct reddish color.

After the leaves have fallen the tree still presents a rather attractive and characteristic appearance. It seldom attains a large size, rarely exceeding twenty-five or thirty feet in height and eight inches in trunk diameter, and having a slender outline due to the rather erect habit of growth of the branches. The bark of the young twigs is smooth and shining, of a reddish-brown color more or less spotted with round, brownish dots. The buds are rather small with loosely imbricated scales, the leaf-buds and flower-buds commonly being found side by side upon the twig. On the larger trees the bark of the trunk is of a dark brown or reddish color, more or less covered with horizontal lines and often having fine scales peeling off the outer surface. The branches and the trunks of the younger trees are very smooth and shine distinctly in the sunlight.

It is in early spring, however, that the Bird Cherry presents its most beautiful appearance. Soon after the white blossoms of the Shadbush have begun to mark the hillsides and the river banks, the dense masses of wonderful bloom appear along the twigs of the Bird Cherry. They are in leafless clusters, each cluster consisting of several small flowers that arise from a short, broad base. The flowers have the structure typical of the Plums and Cherries, and are freely visited by a great variety of insects. They have a distinct and rather pleasing odor, and during the few days of their existence they render the trees the most beautiful and conspicuous objects in the landscape.

The Bird Cherry is essentially a Northern species, extending from the far North south to Pennsylvania, Illinois, and Iowa.

CHOKE CHERRY
PRUNUS VIRGINIANA

THE CHOKE CHERRY

THE Choke Cherry is much more likely to be found as a shrub than as a tree. In the former condition it is very generally distributed over a vast range, extending from the Hudson Bay region on the north to Georgia, Texas, and Mexico on the south. When it takes on the tree-like form it rarely exceeds a height of twenty-five feet or a trunk diameter of six inches. The tree is readily distinguished from the Black Cherry by its reddish fruit and its broader leaves, with sharply-pointed serrations along their margins, these points not turning forward as do those of the margins of the Black Cherry.

The leaves of the Choke Cherry are dull green above and lighter below. In autumn they turn reddish orange or yellowish orange, gradually changing to brown, with petioles and midribs of a magenta or crimson color. After the leaves have fallen the young branches have a rather characteristic appearance which enables one readily to recognize them: the bark is of a grayish-brown or reddish-brown color spotted with lighter colored oval dots. The buds are of good size, pointed and conical, with brown, smooth, imbricated scales. The bark is bitter to the taste and has a characteristic odor.

The Choke Cherries blossom in May and for a brief period take on a beautiful appearance, on account of the white racemes of small flowers. These flowers are very similar to those of the Black Cherry and are visited by great numbers of insects. They soon pass by, however, and are succeeded by small green cherries that slowly develop through the summer until by the end of August they reach their full size and assume the dull red color of maturity. These cherries are eaten by many birds, but have a curiously astringent taste which has given the species its common name.

The Choke Cherry is much more subject to attack by the black knot than is the Black Cherry. It is almost universally disfigured by the strange excrescences of this curious disease, which is so strong a menace to cultivated cherries and plums that it is not worth while to attempt to plant this species for ornamental purposes. It is rather desirable, in all regions where fruit-growing is to be encouraged, that the shrubs should be exterminated from along the roadsides or in the pastures, where they serve as a propagating-ground for insect and fungus pests. A fact to be borne always in mind, however, is that as the leaves of the newly cut bushes wilt they develop a powerful poison that often causes the death of domestic animals that eat them when in the wilted condition. Consequently the newly cut brush should always be piled where it cannot be reached by cattle.

THE WILD BLACK CHERRY

THE Black Cherry is one of the best known and most widely distributed of the wild fruit trees. It is found in all kinds of situations, ranging on the north from Nova Scotia to North Dakota, and on the south from Florida to Texas, and even extending into Mexico and Central America. It is generally readily distinguished from the closely related Choke Cherry by its more tree-like form, more slender leaves, and the slightly-rounded serrations of the leaf-margins. When in fruit it is at once known by the shining black color of the small round drupes.

The leaves of the Black Cherry are of a shining green color on the upper surface and somewhat lighter on the under surface. They hang downward from the horizontal twigs in a very characteristic fashion. In autumn they turn first yellow, then orange, the petioles and midribs becoming a rather brilliant magenta or crimson color.

The fruit of the Black Cherry is often produced in abundance and serves to attract great numbers of robins and other birds that feed eagerly upon it. The cherries ripen late in summer and have, as compared with the choke cherries, a rather agreeable taste. They were formerly used in making a kind of rum, which gave to the tree as one of its common names that of the Rum Cherry.

The winter-twigs are rather easily recognized after one has become familiar with their appearance. The bark is reddish brown thickly spotted with round white dots, and the pointed conical buds have smooth, shining, reddish-brown scales. The bark is intensely bitter to the taste, with a very characteristic odor when bruised.

It is in May or early June that the Black Cherry puts on the crowning glory of its blossoms. The beautiful cylindrical racemes of small white flowers are sure to attract the attention of everyone, even as they attract the visits of innumerable hosts of insects of many orders.

The chief disadvantages of the Black Cherry for the purposes of the landscape gardener are its liability to attack by insects, especially the familiar tent-caterpillar, and to attack by the fungus which produces the peculiar excrescences on the branches known as black knot. It has, however, so many advantages that it is occasionally worth while to combat these enemies in order to enjoy the beauty of the trees and to use them as a lure to birds. There is generally little difficulty in getting wild seedlings to transplant. One horticultural variety has been developed, a weeping form of doubtful utility.

WILD BLACK CHERRY

PRUNUS SEROTINA

RED BUD — JUDAS TREE

THE RED BUD OR JUDAS TREE

THE Red Bud is of interest for many reasons, one of the most important of which is that, while it is indigenous only in the Southern States, it is hardy when planted as an ornamental tree in the Northern States. It seems to be especially a tree of the underwoods, thriving in the shade of the forest and giving to it during the brief period of blossoming a striking beauty by means of its myriads of pink blossoms upon the bare brown branches. These flowers show that the tree belongs to the great family of legumes, each having essentially the structure of a pea- or bean-blossom, and each being succeeded by a fruit-pod which also shows the family relationship of the tree. These pods, which are illustrated on the plate, commonly reach a length of three inches and are often of a light rose color. They generally remain upon the tree through the autumn, commonly being broken off early in winter, and contain generally about a dozen small brown, somewhat flattened seeds.

The habit of growth of the Red Bud has been likened to that of an Apple tree, and a glance at the plate will show the justness of the comparison. When growing in the underwoods the resemblance is likely to be often more striking, because the central vertical shoot is not likely to be so well marked as in the tree of the picture. The surface of the bark is scaly and of a red-brown color. The tree seldom reaches a greater height than forty feet. It is especially valuable in landscape planting on account of its ability to grow in the shade of taller trees, so that it may be occupied to fill in a space between shrubby undergrowth next the ground and tall trees which branch high up. The foliage is clean and attractive, and during the blossoming period the tree is likely to be the most conspicuous feature of the landscape. This species is often called by the name of Judas Tree, a term which appears to be due to the fancied resemblance to the European and Asiatic species, to which this name is given because of the tradition that the blossoming tree was blushing for having been the tree upon which Judas hanged himself.

The Japanese or Chinese Red Bud (*Cercis Chinensis*) is with us generally a beautiful shrub, though a tree in its native home. Its purplish pink flowers are larger than those of the American form and more abundant than the European species. Consequently this is particularly desirable for landscape planting.

THE KENTUCKY COFFEE TREE

IT is easy to see that this curious species is closely related to the much more familiar and widely distributed Honey Locust. Evidence of this relationship is shown in the enormous compound leaves, as well as in the large fruit-pods, the latter being much shorter and thicker than the pods of the Honey Locust. The present species grows in the rich bottom lands of the great south-central region bordered by New York, Pennsylvania, Ontario, Nebraska, Arkansas, and Tennessee. It seems everywhere to be a comparatively rare and local species which, however, is sure to attract attention from the most indifferent observer. It sometimes reaches a height of a hundred feet with a trunk diameter of two or three feet, although of course it is generally of much smaller dimensions. The leaves are often three feet long and of a characteristic doubly compound appearance, shown in the picture on the middle of the plate. The pollen-bearing and the seed-bearing flowers are upon separate trees. The former are in much shorter clusters than the latter, all of the blossoms being greenish white in color. The fruit-pods reach a size of four to eight inches and a width of about two inches. Within each pod are a half dozen or more rather large seeds, in the midst of a curious sweetish pulp which is suggestive of the pulp found in the seed-pods of the Honey Locust.

The winter appearance of the Coffee Tree is not attractive, on account of the absence of small branches and apparently of even the buds upon the large branches. These buds, like those of our common Locust, are almost hidden beneath the bark. It seems a marvel that the gigantic leaves can come from such inconspicuous objects. The leaves are not sent out until late and the flowers do not develop until June. The common name of the species is due to the fact that the early settlers in Kentucky utilized the seeds in place of the coffee berry, but they did not prove a satisfactory substitute and the practice was soon abandoned. The species is often planted in the North as an ornamental tree, and it adds at least the interest of variety to any landscape in which it is planted.

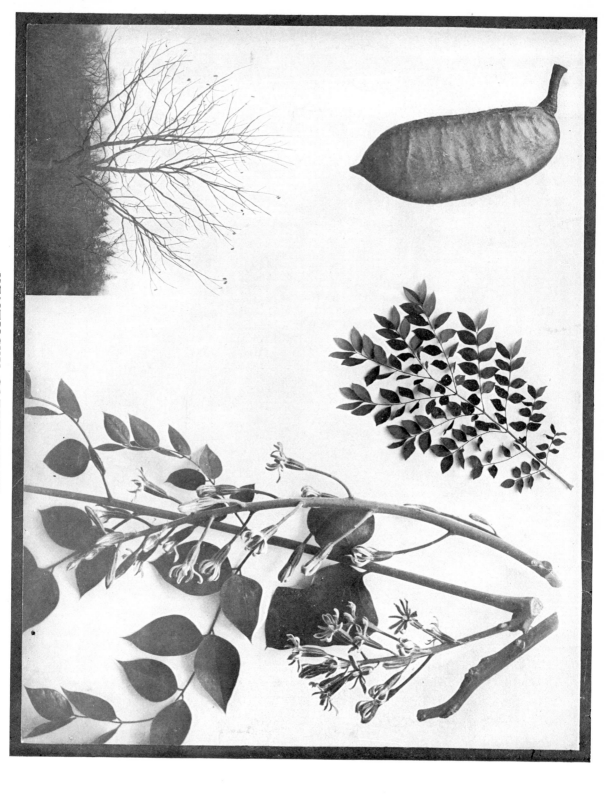

KENTUCKY COFFEE-TREE
GYMNOCLADUS DIOICUS

HONEY LOCUST — HONEY SHUCKS
GLEDITSIA TRIACANTHOS

LEGUMINOSÆ

THE HONEY LOCUST

THOUGH very generally planted as a shade and ornamental tree, the Honey Locust is indigenous to a region bounded by Alabama and Pennsylvania on the east, Michigan and Minnesota on the north, Kansas and Nebraska on the west, and Texas, Mississippi, and Alabama on the south. In this great area the tree grows chiefly near the rivers, generally singly, though occasionally in groves of considerable extent. Along the Atlantic coast the extensive introduction of the species has led it to become naturalized in many places.

By several distinctive characters you may know the Honey Locust. The surest sign at any season is found in the great compound thorns which stud the bark of the twigs, branches and even the trunk. None of our other trees have such formidable weapons of defence. Through the summer the doubly compound leaves are also distinctive, while in early autumn the great fruit-pods are unmistakable.

When growing in its favorite position in a rich intervale this tree assumes a broadly open form, more or less flattened at the top. In such situations it may reach a height of more than a hundred feet and a trunk diameter of four or five feet. The outer bark is grayish black, hard in texture, with vertical furrows more or less numerous, the bark between the furrows being somewhat scaly. On younger trees the bark is smooth and beautiful and of a dark gray color.

The greenish blossoms come out with the young leaves in June in small racemes, the pollen-bearing and the pistil-bearing flowers being generally on different trees, or different branches of the same tree. The great seed-pods begin to fall early in autumn. They are flattened and sometimes reach a length of eighteen inches with a width of from one to one and a half inches. The general color is a dull leathery brown with more or less of a reddish tone. The chocolate-brown seeds are usually numerous; they are arranged in indistinct cells in the upper half of the pod, the lower third of which has between the two walls a curious juicy, greenish-yellow pulp, rather sweet in taste.

The Honey Locust is valuable as an ornamental tree for many reasons. It is hardy, free from disease, easily propagated, and a rapid grower. The objectionable thorns are now obviated in a thornless variety offered by nurserymen.

THE YELLOW-WOOD OR VIRGILIA

O F all the trees of the eastern region of North America this seems to be the rarest and most local in its distribution. Were it not that it has been frequently planted in parks and ornamental grounds as far north as New England, it would be a species which comparatively few people would ever see. This very fact of its rarity, as well as the interesting character of its flowers, fruit and foliage, renders it especially desirable for ornamental planting. It is indigenous in a comparatively limited region of the Southern States, its distribution being given in Professor Sargent's authoritative "Manual of The Trees of North America" in these words: "Limestone cliffs and ridges, generally in rich soil, and often overhanging the banks of mountain streams; Central Kentucky and Central Tennessee to Northern Alabama and the western slopes of the high mountains of Eastern Tennessee; to Cherokee County, North Carolina; rare and local; most abundant and of its largest size in the neighborhood of Nashville, Tennessee."

The general habit of the tree as it grows in the open is well shown in the picture on the plate. The division into several large branches a short distance from the ground is quite characteristic of the species, as is the broad open effect produced by the rather slender, more or less horizontal branches. Beautiful white flowers, which show at once that this tree belongs to the great family of leguminous plants, blossom in June and are succeeded by the slender pods, which are equally distinctive in showing the family relationship. The large compound leaves are of especial interest in that the base of the petiole completely covers the bud, a condition which is more familiar to most of us in the case of the Sycamore or Buttonwood. The leaves are also interesting from the fact that the leaflets are arranged in alternate fashion along the central stalk, a condition which is very unusual, as may readily be seen by glancing at those plates which show the other kinds of trees with compound leaves, in which the leaflets are opposite each other along the central stalk. The wood is of a characteristic yellow color sometimes more or less brownish, which gives the species its common name. It is heavy and hard, weighing thirty-nine pounds per cubic foot. The tree is also sometimes called the Virgilia.

YELLOW WOOD — VIRGILIA

CLADRASTIS LUTEA

COMMON LOCUST — ACACIA
ROBINIA PSEUDACACIÆ

THE COMMON LOCUST OR ACACIA

ALTHOUGH originally native to a comparatively small area along the sides of the Alleghany Mountains in Pennsylvania and Georgia, the Common Locust is now probably the best known and most generally distributed arborescent form of the great family of plants having leguminous fruits. For very many years it has been widely planted as a shade tree, and in most instances it has spread by means of underground stems, so that the original tree is often represented by thickets or groves of large or small trees that occupy considerable areas.

There are many characteristics that distinguish the Common Locust. In winter the peculiar paired spines with the bud hidden between them in the midst of the broad, rounded leaf-scar, serve at once to identify the branches. In spring and throughout the summer the beautiful pinnately compound leaves, having a central terminal leaflet, are sufficiently distinctive and with the habit of growth of the tree serve to give an impression of grace and strength that is very pleasing In early summer the beautiful racemes of fragrant white flowers attract universal attention from the world of insects, as well as from that of man, while after the leaves have fallen in autumn the hundreds of clustered pods give a distinctive character to the tree as far as it can be seen. The bark of the trunk is dark brown, often with a slightly reddish tinge, more or less vertically furrowed and sometimes largely covered with squarish scales.

This Locust is more subject to attack by insects than almost any other tree which is commonly planted for ornamental purposes. The trunk serves as the breeding-place of the beautiful beetle called the locust-borer, while the leaves serve a similar purpose for several species of leaf-miners and other leaf-eating insects. As a result the trees seldom flourish as they ought to do and are very likely to be disfigured and unsightly. This fact seriously interferes with their value in landscape gardening, and naturally is leading to the substitution of other species. In Europe there are a number of horticultural forms which are propagated by grafting that appear to be quite generally used in landscape planting. The type form is easily propagated by means of seeds.

THE CLAMMY LOCUST

THE Clammy Locust is easily distinguished by the viscid exudation on the twigs, pods and leaf-stalks. It is a more southern form than the Common Locust, being native to the mountainous regions of Virginia, Georgia, and the Carolinas. It is also a smaller species, the trees seldom attaining a height greater than forty feet, and in the North generally much less than this. The flower-clusters are also strikingly different, being shorter and more compact and of a beautiful pale rose color instead of white; they appear noticeably later in the season than those of the Common Locust. As will be seen from the pictures, the leaves are very similar in the two species.

The flowers of both these Locusts are adapted to pollination by bees, especially bumble-bees, which visit them freely. It would not be strange if it frequently happened that a bee would go from one kind of tree to the other if flowers of both should be present at the same time, and that in consequence a natural hybrid should result. Perhaps this is the origin of the beautiful variety of Locust called *bella-rosea*, which is much in favor for ornamental planting. It is commonly considered a variety of the Common Locust, and is believed to have resulted from a crossing of the two species.

Another locust-like shrub is very commonly planted in ornamental landscapes: it is the Rose Acacia, and is known technically as *Robinia hispida*. It is a very hairy plant, and has long racemes of beautiful rose-colored flowers. Originally native to nearly the same region as the Clammy Locust, it fortunately is hardy in the North and is very useful in making thickets by means of underground stems. It is at once distinguished by the hairs that give the growing parts almost a moss-covered appearance. It is sometimes called the Bristly Locust.

In the extreme Southwestern States there is a shrub-like Locust, called commonly the New Mexican Locust and technically *Robinia Neo-Mexicana*. It sometimes becomes a tree twenty-five feet high, and bears rose-colored flowers. The pods are hairy but not viscid as are those of the Clammy Locust.

All of these Locusts have flowers closely resembling those of the peas and beans of our gardens, and pod-like fruits resembling the fruits of these familiar vegetables. This fact enables the botanists to classify them in the great family of legumes, which includes many of our most important plants, both wild and cultivated.

VELVET SUMACH — STAGHORN SUMACH

THE STAGHORN SUMACH OR VELVET SUMACH

OF the several species of Sumach that add so much beauty to American landscapes the Velvet or Staghorn Sumach is the one which is most likely to take on the size and dignity of a tree. It is always to be known at any season of the year by the dense growth of velvety hairs upon the bark of the younger branches. The long petioles of the compound leaves are similarly clothed. The leaflets are regularly, though not deeply, serrate on the margins. In autumn the leaves assume most brilliant colors commonly becoming an intense red which is almost scarlet. The dense panicles of flowers appear on the ends of short branches early in summer. The pollen-bearing and the seed-bearing blossoms are separate, the former coming into flower about a week in advance of the latter. The general color in each case is greenish yellow, more or less tinged with reddish. The flowers are very freely visited by a great variety of insects, which serve as pollen-carriers. The fruit matures early in autumn, becoming of a brilliant crimson color, the large panicles of which are familiar to everyone.

The Staghorn Sumach often reaches a height of thirty or forty feet and is commonly used to great advantage in landscape planting. It serves admirably as a background for low shrubbery, and always has a decided decorative value. In spring and summer the long green leaves give an effect of tropical luxuriance, while in autumn the crimson foliage and fruit are unsurpassed for brilliance of coloring. Even in winter, when the leaves have fallen and most of the fruits have broken off, its velvety twigs with their characteristic mode of branching are attractive and interesting. The wood is strongly yellow in color. Like the other Sumachs this species spreads rapidly from suckers, which are easily transplanted. During recent years a cut-leaved variety has been introduced, which is exceedingly desirable as an ornamental plant.

The Staghorn Sumach seems most at home in the Atlantic Coast States, although it has a range extending from New Brunswick to Minnesota on the north, and Mississippi to Alabama on the south. It is a hardy species, notably free from attack by insect or fungus enemies.

THE DWARF SUMACH

THE distinctive character of the Dwarf Sumach lies in the curiously-winged blades of the stem of the compound leaf, a feature that is clearly shown on the accompanying plate. Even in winter one can generally find some of these leaf-stalks on or beneath the branches so that the identification of the species is easy and certain. It may be seen also from the picture that the margins of the leaflets are entire, though sometimes there is a slight serration toward the tip. The upper surface of the blades of the leaflets is smooth and shining, while the lower surface is more or less pubescent, as are the leaf-stalks and the young shoots. The dense panicles of greenish blossoms appear in summer later than those of the other Sumachs. The fruit is red and covered with hairs, as in the case of the Smooth and the Staghorn Sumachs. It remains upon the tree through the autumn, and often until the following spring, furnishing food to a number of winter birds.

In most regions this species assumes only a shrubby growth, covering large areas with its brilliant foliage, which in autumn becomes a glorious red—the finest in coloring of all the Sumachs. But sometimes in the mountainous regions of the Southwest it takes on the form of a tree, occasionally reaching a height of thirty feet and a trunk diameter of ten inches. The plant is widely distributed, occurring in the United States from Maine to Florida on the east, and from Nebraska to Texas on the west. Over most of this vast area it deserves the name Dwarf Sumach, rising but a few feet from the ground, and spreading over hillsides and barren lands by means of horizontal stems just below the soil surface.

Its value in glorifying the autumn landscape indicates that the Dwarf Sumach may be utilized to advantage in landscape gardening, an idea which is often carried out by landscape artists in Europe as well as in America. There is a considerable percentage of tannin in the leaves and bark, and in the Southern States these are often collected and ground, the product being used in tanning leather.

DWARF SUMACH
RHUS COPALLINA

SMOOTH SUMACH

RHUS GLABRA

THE SMOOTH SUMACH

WHEN you find a native Sumach with reddish hairy fruit, smooth leaves and twigs, and leaf-stems without winged margins, you may be sure it is the Smooth Sumach. As may be seen in the plate, the margins of the leaflets are slightly serrate and their tips are slender and acutely pointed. The under surface of the leaflets is whitish, the upper surface being bright green and turning to brilliant red in autumn. The panicles of greenish flowers appear about midsummer and the scarlet fruit remains on throughout the winter, furnishing a starvation ration to chickadees and other winter birds.

The Smooth Sumach is commonly a shrub rather than a tree. It is distributed over a great area, extending from Nova Scotia to Florida on the east, and from British Columbia to Arizona on the west. It is very commonly associated with the Staghorn Sumach, which is at once distinguished by the velvety covering of hairs on the twigs. Both of these species, like other common members of the genus Rhus, have the power of multiplying by underground stems—a fact that enables them to cover sandy barrens and rocky hillsides to the exclusion of other shrubs, and commonly to the great enhancement of the beauty of the autumn landscape.

Like the other Sumachs, the twigs of this species very commonly die toward the tip each winter, especially when the weather has been favorable to growth late the previous season. The result is that the branch is continued from a side bud some distance down from the tip, so that the twig is likely to show a very zig-zag sort of growth. The bark of the stems near the ground is often completely gnawed off in winter by mice that work beneath the snow.

The leaves of the Smooth Sumach are sometimes used in tanning leather, and the shrubs are often utilized by landscape architects for ornamental planting. For this purpose, however, a variety which is believed to be a sport from the normal form is much more valuable; it is called the Fern-leaved Sumach, and has very attractive laciniate foliage that colors as brilliantly in autumn as does the parent type. This form makes a very beautiful border plant, although some trouble may come from its spreading to adjacent lawns, if care is not taken to prevent the underground stems from penetrating in all directions.

THE DOGWOOD OR POISON SUMACH

FORTUNATELY the Poison Sumach can be easily known at any season: in summer and autumn the many leaflets with smooth margins and with the main leaf-stalk not winged enable one to identify the species; in winter and spring, the grayish-white berries in drooping clusters and the smooth bark of the branches serve a similar purpose. The importance of knowing and avoiding the plant need not be urged upon any one who has been poisoned, or has known others to be poisoned, by its leaves or twigs. For this is the most virulent of our contact-poisoning plants and its effects upon persons susceptible to harm from it are often very severe. It is not always necessary even that it be touched; the mere passing by has been known to cause the characteristic irritation of the skin. Some people, however, are immune and may handle all parts of the shrub with impunity. In general the danger seems greatest when one is perspiring freely.

As a rule the Poison Sumach is a branching shrub ten to fifteen feet high, growing in groups which are likely to attract attention by the brilliant beauty of their autumnal foliage. Frequently, however, it grows into a small tree, perhaps twenty feet high. It is generally to be found along the borders of swamps, and occurs over a great region, extending from Maine to Alabama on the east, and Minnesota to Louisiana on the west. As compared with the other Sumachs, the flowers, which blossom in early summer, are in small clusters.

In his "Report on the Trees and Shrubs of Massachusetts," George B. Emerson wrote many years ago: "The near resemblance in all the properties of the Poison Sumach to those of the Varnish-yielding Sumach of Japan, has led to the belief that a similar substance might be procured from it. To this end Dr. Bigelow made, in 1815, several experiments which seem to establish this point in a manner very satisfactory. A quantity of the juice was boiled alone, until nearly all the volatile oil had escaped, and the remainder was reduced almost to the state of a resin. In this state it was applied while warm to several substances, which after cooling exhibited the most brilliant, glossy, jet-black surface. The coating appeared very durable and firm, and was not affected by moisture. It was elastic and perfectly opaque, and seemed to answer the purposes of both paint and varnish. The poisonous property, as in most cases of vegetable poisons, seems to be removed by evaporation or boiling, and the dry varnish would probably be innocuous."

The species has other names than Poison Sumach: in some localities it is the Dogwood or Poison Dogwood; in others it is the Poison Elder or the Poison Ash. It has also at least two accepted scientific names: in Sargent's Manual, Linné's *Rhus vernix* is accepted; in the "Cyclopedia of Horticulture" De Candolle's *R. venenata* is used.

POISON SUMACH — POISON DOGWOOD

RHUS VERNIX

AILANTHUS

AILANTHUS GLANDULOSA

THE AILANTHUS

THE Ailanthus, or Tree of Heaven, has been quite extensively planted in parks and private grounds throughout the Eastern States. It is a distinctive tree which grows very rapidly, and has extraordinarily long compound leaves that often reach a length of three feet. Even the leaflets are commonly five inches long, and have the basal part of the margins coarsely toothed while the terminal part is entire. Each tooth bears at its point on the lower surface a curious gland. The leaves retain their green hue quite late in autumn. When they fall they reveal branches of a very characteristic size and form. The young shoots are very large and have leaf-scars which are also of an unusual size. These leaf-scars are irregularly shield-shaped and have a grayish surface. The broad, rounded buds have the reddish or brownish scales covered with whitish down.

The Ailanthus comes into flower in June, the pollen-bearing and the seed-bearing blossoms developing on different trees. The former have an intensely disagreeable odor, which has led people very generally to cut down the trees bearing them, while trees bearing the latter, which are practically odorless, have been allowed to grow. As will be seen from the two sprays lying along the leaf in the picture—the right-hand one being the pollen-bearing, the left-hand one the seed-bearing—the two kinds of flowers bear a general resemblance to each other and develop in sparse panicles which are quite characteristic. The pollen-bearing panicles drop off after blossoming, while the seed-bearing ones gradually mature into the curiously interesting and beautiful winged fruits, the presence of which give to the tree in autumn one of its most attractive features. These fruits are illustrated in the upper left-hand corner of the plate and have near their middle an enlarged part which holds the seeds. These fruits are admirably adapted to dispersal by the wind, and have led to the spontaneous appearance of the Ailanthus in many parts of the East and South.

This tree is a native of China and is sometimes called the Chinese Sumach. It seems to have been first planted in America in 1820 on Long Island, and many of the trees planted early have reached a height of sixty or seventy feet and a trunk diameter of four or five feet. Its chief disadvantages for ornamental planting, in addition to that of the vile-smelling blossoms, are its tendency to sucker and to penetrate wells and cisterns with its roots which give the water a nauseating taste.

THE AMERICAN HOLLY

GREAT numbers of people are familiar with the leaves and fruit of the American Holly who have never seen the growing tree. This of course is due to the very general use of the branches for holiday decorations, and to the fact that the tree is a local species in many parts of the United States, occurring especially in peat-bogs and along rich river-bottoms, although in the more northern parts of its range it is often found in dryer soil. It is indigenous from Massachusetts to Florida, and in the Mississippi Valley from Indiana to the Gulf of Mexico. It occurs as far west as Eastern Texas, where it attains its largest size. It is occasionally planted as an ornamental tree throughout its range, being hardy as far north as Massachusetts. It is difficult to transplant successfully and is of slow growth but nevertheless it is so beautiful a tree that it is worth while to utilize it in landscape planting for the adornment of the undergrowth of groves, either along the margins or beneath the larger trees.

The general characteristics of the American Holly may be seen by a glance at the plate. The small greenish white flowers appear in May or June, the pollen-bearing and the seed-bearing being in different groups generally upon separate trees. As is usually the case, the former grow in thicker clusters to which insects are attracted, these visitors carrying the pollen to the seed-bearing flowers. In due time the latter develop into the well-known beautiful red fruits scattered singly on short stalks along the twigs. The evergreen leaves, with their spinous margins and smooth, shining surfaces, are of an essentially decorative form and seem especially designed for use in Christmas greenery. This custom is of great antiquity, dating at least back to early Roman times, and very likely to an even earlier practice "of hanging the interior of dwellings with evergreens as a refuge for sylvan spirits from the inclemency of the weather."

In Europe the closely related European Holly, which is very similar to our species, is the plant that is most largely employed for this purpose.

AMERICAN HOLLY
ILEX OPACA

MOUNTAIN MAPLE
ACER SPICATUM

THE MOUNTAIN MAPLE

TO those fortunate people who are privileged to spend their summer vacations in the mountainous parts of New England the Mountain Maple is a most familiar sight. Over large regions of territory these shrubs or small trees are found along every highway as well as by the margins of every trout-brook, pond or lake. With the Striped Maple it forms the most characteristic feature of the underwoods, and is usually more abundant than the latter species. As a tree it seldom reaches a greater height than twenty or twenty-five feet, and it is mainly a Northern species, occurring throughout the great region south of Nova Scotia and Newfoundland and extending along mountainous elevations as far as Georgia.

The leaves of the Mountain Maple average a much smaller size than do those of the Striped Maple, although they are somewhat similar in form and texture. There seem to be more of them on the twigs and one soon learns to distinguish between the two at a glance. The new twigs in early summer are grayish and more or less downy, but after the leaves fall in autumn the smaller branches are of a distinct crimson color which is most characteristic. Near at hand one sees that the red bark of these twigs is covered with a distinct whitish pubescence which serves to distinguish the Mountain Maple from all other species. Before falling in autumn the leaves turn to a deep red color.

The blossoms of the Mountain Maple do not develop until early in summer, after the leaves have reached their full size. These blossoms are borne on the ends of the new season's twigs in racemes, which have the appearance of panicles and are not so drooping as is the case with most of the other Maples. There is the same variability as to staminate and pistillate flowers that is found in the Striped Maple, and the fruit matures very slowly through the summer, ripening in autumn and often remaining upon the trees well into the winter.

During the summer months these fruits take on most wonderful hues of red and furnish one of the most attractive features of the landscape. The individual samaras are smaller than those of any other of our native Maples and are borne on slender, thread-like pedicels.

It seems strange that the Mountain Maple is not more largely used in landscape gardening. At all seasons of the year it furnishes beautiful coloring. It is eminently hardy, and is not likely to grow too high for effective use among shrubbery. It apparently is entirely free from insect and fungus enemies, and it certainly has sufficient merit to be extensively planted.

THE STRIPED MAPLE OR MOOSEWOOD

IN the more northern States the Striped Maple is one of the most distinctive features of what Stevenson so happily called the "underwoods." As one wanders through the trails along the mountainsides one constantly sees the slender saplings of this beautiful little tree springing up beneath the monarchs of the forest, and occasionally in an open glade reaching a considerable size.

In summer the Striped Maple is easily recognized by the large goosefoot-like leaves, with extraordinarily thin blades and a most delicate network of veins and veinlets. The upper surface is dark yellow-green while the lower surface is much lighter, the latter being sparsely clothed with short rust-red hairs. The margins are finely, doubly serrate and the three lobes have delicate acuminate points. About the time they fall in autumn the leaves change to a bright yellow color.

In its winter condition the Striped Maple is easily recognized by the beautiful striped markings of the bark, which is generally some hue of green or red. The bark is smooth and the buds have short stalks which are quite characteristic.

In spring or early in summer, just after the leaves have developed, the beautiful pendent racemes of yellow flowers appear. Like so many of the Maples, these blossoms are variable as to the pollen-bearing and the seed-bearing florets. For the most part each raceme consists of one kind of flower, although racemes of both sorts are commonly to be found upon the same tree. Each small bell-shaped flower hangs on a slender stem and has both sepals and petals of a greenish-yellow color. The seed-bearing flowers gradually develop into racemes of key-fruits that mature early in autumn, each pair of key-fruits being united at a wide angle.

The Striped Maple is often called the Moosewood because the branches are fed upon by the moose, a name, however, which is also applied to the Hobble-bush. The tree seldom attains a height of more than twenty-five feet. It is essentially a Northern species, extending from the far North, south to the mountains of Tennessee and the Carolinas.

STRIPED MAPLE — MOOSEWOOD

ACER PENNSYLVANICUM

SUGAR MAPLE — ROCK MAPLE

ACER SACCHARUM

THE SUGAR MAPLE OR ROCK MAPLE

TO one whose youth was spent in a sugar-making region this Maple must always recall fond memories of the old "sap places" where, in the uncertain weather of early spring, the trickling juices of the trees were converted into delicious sugar. This qualification of the species distinguishes it from all the other eastern Maples and gives it a unique position even to-day, when maple syrup rather than sugar is the chief product into which the sap is converted. This Maple is however, also of extraordinary value as a source of lumber and fuel, and is perhaps the most generally planted of all our shade trees.

The Sugar Maple is easily distinguished at any season of the year. In winter the opposite branches, tipped with sharply pointed conical buds, are distinct and characteristic. In spring the beautiful yellow-green blossoms in pendent clusters are very different from those of any of the other Maples. In summer the broad leaves with their rounded sinuses, without the milky stem-juices of the Norway Maple, enable one to identify the species at a glance. And in autumn the characteristic key-fruits and brilliant yellow, orange and red leaves serve a similar purpose. In the woods the trees grow straight and tall, often attaining a great height and a diameter of several feet. In open situations they develop a wide expanse of foliage, which serves to make them ideal for shade. The bark on young trees is rather smooth, but on the old trees it is deeply furrowed with vertical ridges and is of a characteristic deep gray color.

The Sugar Maple is also commonly called the Rock Maple and the Hard Maple. The typical form is found throughout the northeastern region of North America, being replaced in the more southern States by a variety having three principal lobes in the leaves. While the blossoms appear in earliest spring the fruits do not ripen until autumn, and occasionally when the season has been dry they hang upon the trees until winter, when they furnish abundant food for the grosbeaks and other winter birds.

In the far West sugar has been successfully made from the Broad-leaved Maple which is a splendid tree in the forests of Oregon. It has a broad leaf with rounded sinuses that are suggestive of those of the Sugar Maple. The fruits do not mature until autumn, although they reach full size by the end of June.

There are various other trees formerly regarded as varieties of the Sugar Maple which are now held to be distinct species. One of these is the Florida Sugar Maple (*Acer Floridanum*) found in Florida and along the Gulf Coast. Another is the Black Maple (*A. nigrum*) widely distributed through the North and frequently replacing the typical Sugar Maple in the West: you may know it by its orange colored twigs. Still another is called *Acer leucoderme* and is found locally in the South, while the Large-toothed Sugar Maple (*A. grandidentatum*) is found locally in the far West.

THE SILVER MAPLE OR WHITE MAPLE

THE Silver Maple or White Maple or Soft Maple, as it is variously called, is one of the best known of the Maples because it is a widely distributed species and has been very generally planted as a shade and ornamental tree. It is always easily distinguished by the white under surface of the leaves and the very characteristic deep sinuses, the bases of the sinuses having smooth margins. As an indigenous species the Silver Maple is especially likely to be found along the banks of rivers and other streams, and it is distributed over a great range from New Brunswick and Ontario, south to Florida and west to the Indian Territory, Nebraska, and Dakota. In the valley of the Ohio River, trees more than a hundred feet high and three or four feet in diameter are often found, but throughout the more northern parts of its range the trees are generally considerably smaller.

The Silver Maple blossoms in earliest spring, usually during the latter part of March, even in the more northern States. The flower-buds are crowded together generally at the ends of short branches, each bud containing from three to five blossoms. For the most part the flowers in a single bud have but one set of essential organs in a well-developed condition. In those blossoms in which the stamens are perfectly developed the pistils are abortive or entirely wanting, while in those flowers in which the pistils are well developed the stamens are abortive or wanting. Sometimes a whole tree will have one kind of blossoms almost entirely ; sometimes a single branch will have one kind of blossoms exclusively, and sometimes a single twig will have both kinds of flowers growing side by side upon its tip. In the pollen-bearing blossoms the part called the calyx is light yellowish green with five rather indistinct lobes and with four to six stamens projecting far beyond the calyx. These pollen-bearing flowers are reddish in color, the color being especially emphasized by the tiny pollen-bags or anthers. The seed-bearing flowers are conspicuous on account of the ends of the pistils being of a crimson color. Although the imported honey-bees may be seen on warm days gathering an abundance of pollen from the flowers, the Silver Maple seems to be essentially a wind-pollenized species. This is indicated by the lack of petals, the sudden maturing of the stamens, the manner of shedding the pollen, and the absence of nectar and odor. The key-fruits develop rapidly and mature late in spring or early in summer.

It is needless to say that the Silver Maple is one of the best trees for street and ornamental planting. Its chief disadvantage is found in the fact that it is a host tree for the Maple-tree bark-louse, a pest that during recent years has become exceedingly troublesome on the shade trees of many cities.

SILVER MAPLE — WHITE MAPLE — RIVER MAPLE

ACER SACCHARINUM

RED MAPLE — SWAMP MAPLE

MAPLE FAMILY

THE RED MAPLE

THE Red Maple is happily so named: at almost any season it displays some token to justify the adjective. In winter it is the bark of the twigs; in spring the blossoms; in summer the key-fruits, while in autumn—

"The Maple swamps glow like a sunset sea,
Each leaf a ripple with its separate flush."

The species is easily distinguished from its allies. The leaves have the sinuses acute rather than rounded. The flowers are on short stalks and the small key-fruits on long stalks that arise from a common base. The young trees have a smooth, distinctive light gray bark, while the old trees have the dark gray bark separated into many long scale-like plates. The wood is less valuable than that of the Sugar Maple, but it is largely used for making chairs and other kinds of furniture.

In many respects the Red Maple is the most conspicuous tree in our landscape. In winter the red twigs often shine in the sunlight, while in earliest spring the deep crimson blossoms so thickly clothe the leafless branches that the trees challenge the attention of the most listless observer. A few weeks later, when the blossoms have developed into fruits, the latter are so deeply crimson that they give color to the landscape just come into the leafy greenness of June. The terminal leaves on the younger growth are commonly crimson through the summer, and in earliest autumn the whole foliage becomes so brilliant as to be the dominant tone of the lower valleys.

The Red Maple is also commonly called the Scarlet Maple, Swamp Maple and Soft Maple. It is a lowland tree, being especially found in swamps and along river-banks, and is widely distributed through eastern North America, occurring both north and south as far west as Iowa and Texas. Professor Sargent states that the largest trees are found in the valley of the Ohio River and its tributaries.

There are two well marked varieties of the Red Maple. One of these named *Drummondii* is found in Louisiana, Arkansas and Texas and is distinguished by three-lobed leaves which are covered on the lower surface with a white, cottony coating, which is also much in evidence on the young twigs. The other variety, called *tridens*, occurs along the coast from New Jersey to Texas, and is generally to be known by its few glandular teeth and the fact that the lower surfaces of the leaves are commonly more or less hairy.

THE ASH-LEAVED MAPLE OR BOX ELDER

PERHAPS the most attractive feature of the Box Elder or Ash-leaved Maple is found in the rich coloring of the twigs in autumn and winter. These are of a glorious olive green, often covered with a glaucous bloom, one of the most satisfying hues in the world of trees. The broad buds are densely downy and generally greenish or brownish in color. The bark of the older branches is greenish or brownish, while that of the trunk varies from yellowish green on young trees to dark grayish brown on older ones.

The pendent clusters of greenish yellow flowers appear in early spring, generally during the first half of April. The pollen-bearing and seed-bearing blossoms are on separate trees. The former are in simple clusters of long-stemmed flowers; the latter are in long racemes. The leaves begin to develop as the blossoms appear, and soon clothe the tree with a compound foliage of a tender green color. Each leaf has from three to seven leaflets, and is of a very characteristic form, which is well shown in the accompanying picture.

As the leaves fall from the Box Elder in October the fruit-laden tree seems scarcely to miss them, so thickly is it clothed with the long pendent racemes of graceful key-fruits. There are often ten or a dozen fruits hanging from a single stalk, the distance from the base of the stalk to the tip of the terminal samara being commonly nine or ten inches. Each pair of fruits is joined at nearly a right angle, each fruit being slender at the base and having a rather broad wing. These key-fruits often remain upon the tree through the greater part of the winter, being whipped off one at a time by strong winds that carry them far and wide and leave behind the stalks still attached to the twigs.

As a shade and ornamental tree the Box Elder has the advantages of rapid growth, dense foliage, good coloring, and comparative freedom from attack by insects and fungi. As it gets older, however, it often shows a certain lack of grace, and in some way it does not make the distinctive appeal to one that many of our shade trees do. It is variable in growth, so that it is not desirable for planting in long rows where uniformity is desired. Of late years varieties with colored foliage have been developed and offered by nurserymen.

As a native tree the Ash-leaved Maple is distributed throughout most of the United States east of the Rocky Mountains. In California a special variety is indigenous.

BOX ELDER — ASH-LEAVED MAPLE

SYCAMORE MAPLE
ACER PSEUDO-PLATANUS

THE SYCAMORE MAPLE

THE Sycamore Maple has been rather extensively planted in the Eastern States as a shade and ornamental tree. It has many advantages for this purpose, being vigorous and hardy, free from insect and fungus enemies, attractive throughout the year and furnishing in summer a very dense shade. It grows rapidly and is easily started from seed.

This tree is readily distinguished at any season from the other Maples. In summer the leaves bear a general resemblance to those of the Red Maple in their outline, but they are much denser in texture and the lobes are broader toward the tip. These leaves are palmately five-lobed but the two basal lobes are commonly so small as to make it practically a three-lobed leaf. The veins are very distinct, especially on the under surface, where they project prominently, and are more or less clothed with fine hairs along their sides. The upper surface of the leaf is dark green, the under surface being decidedly lighter, and the whole blade changing in autumn to a distinct yellow color. The fruit matures in autumn, being borne in long clusters with rather small key-fruits. After the leaves have fallen the bare tree presents a sturdy appearance, with the large green buds as its most distinctive character. In spring the long drooping racemes of blossoms hanging from the ends of the young branches are very distinctive. The young leaves as they push out are covered on the under surface with a dense cottony down.

In Mrs. Dyson's interesting little English book, "The Stories of the Trees," may be found an account of the origin of the name commonly given to this species, which in Europe seems to be generally called simply the Sycamore, although this term is more properly applied to the plane-tree:

"In the miracle plays, it seems, one of the favorite scenes for acting was the flight of Joseph and Mary into Egypt, and one legend said that on their way they rested under a sycamore tree. No sycamores, however, grew in the countries where these plays were acted and so our sycamore was chosen in its place because its shady leaves were a little like those of the true sycamore, and ever since then it has borne the name of the tree whose place it took. Before that time it was called the *mock-plane* because its leaves were the same shape as the plane-tree leaves, and by that name it is still known in some places."

THE NORWAY MAPLE

AMONG the shade trees which have been introduced into America from Europe the Norway Maple easily stands in the front rank. It is a thrifty, hardy species, able to survive many of the dangers which beset a city shade tree. It has thick, firm leaves of attractive shape and color, which remain upon the trees considerably later than do those of the native Maples. In early spring the flowers render the tree conspicuous and attractive, and throughout the season the developing fruits add a decided charm to the foliage.

In general outline the leaves of the Norway Maple resemble those of the Sugar Maple, although they may easily be distinguished by the fact that the basal lobes of the former extend much further out than do those of the latter. This fact gives to the main part of the blade a characteristic rectangular appearance which helps in its recognition. A more certain test for the novice, however, is to break off a petiole and if there exudes from the broken ends a milky sap it is surely the Norway Maple. The blossoms of the Norway Maple are very different from those of any other species. They appear just before or at the time of the development of the leaves, in short corymbose clusters of a yellow-green color that render a well-developed tree one of the most conspicuous objects in a spring landscape. The flowers are commonly monœcious and are particularly interesting on account of the large nectar disc at the base of each blossom. After the petals have dropped the key-fruits slowly mature, increasing rather rapidly in size during the middle or last of June, by which time they have generally reached their full length, although the seed does not fully ripen until late in summer or early in autumn. Many of the key-fruits remain upon the trees until after the leaves drop off.

These key-fruits of the Norway Maple are larger and more beautiful in form than those of any of the native species. They are united at a very wide angle so that the general effect is horizontal, and they have a grace of outline which is exceedingly attractive. It would be worth while to plant a tree of this species just for the sake of seeing every year these key-fruits during the long months of their development.

The bark of the mature tree is dark gray in color and thickly marked with narrow vertical ridges having rather deep furrows between them. The outer bark clings closely to the inner, and the general effect is quite characteristic. The tree grows native over a large part of Europe and is offered very generally for sale by American nurserymen.

NORWAY MAPLE

OHIO BUCKEYE
ÆSCULUS GLABRA

THE OHIO BUCKEYE

ONE who is not familiar with the characteristics of this celebrated tree will easily infer, after a study of the pictures on the plate, that it is closely related to the more generally known Horse-Chestnut. This relationship is shown in the character of the leaves and blossoms, of the fruit-husk and nut, as well as of the winter-twigs. The leaves differ in having generally but five leaflets, as well as in their outlines. The flowers differ in being much smaller and more crowded on the twigs, and in their pale yellow-green color. The fruit is generally smaller, as are the winter-buds and leaf-scars.

The Ohio Buckeye thrives best in the fertile soil of the rich bottomlands of the great central western region of the United States. It extends on the east to Pennsylvania and Alabama, and on the west to Iowa, Kansas, and the Indian Territory, rarely occuring further north than Ohio. It occasionally reaches a height of seventy feet and a trunk diameter of two feet, but generally it is much smaller, commonly having a height of twenty to thirty feet. The wood is soft and light, weighing but twenty-eight pounds per cubic foot, and has occasionally been used for various manufacturing purposes. The nuts of the Buckeye are reputed to be poisonous to various domestic animals, and in consequence the trees have been very generally cut down in regions where they formerly grew. This partially accounts for the fact that natives of the Buckeye State are often totally unfamiliar with the tree. The name Buckeye is due to the fact that the partially-opened shell gives a glimpse of the brown nut and its paler scar which is very suggestive of the eye of the deer: and the species was called the Ohio Buckeye by the naturalist Michaux because he found it especially abundant along the banks of the Ohio River. It is supposed that Ohio came to be called the Buckeye State from the name thus applied to the tree.

This tree is well worthy of being planted occasionally to give variety and interest in landscape gardening. It will endure the climate as far north as Massachusetts. It is sometimes called the Fetid Buckeye, probably on account of the odor of the blossoms.

THE HORSE-CHESTNUT

FROM its original home in the mountains of Greece the Horse-Chestnut has been carried by men over a large part of the habitable world. From the earliest settlement of North America by Europeans it has been commonly planted for shade and ornament, and in some parts of the Eastern States it has spread spontaneously from the fruit of these planted trees.

The Horse-Chestnut has many qualities which make it desirable for ornamental planting. It grows sturdily and rapidly, has few insect enemies, gives a dense shade, and has at all seasons a somewhat conventional beauty that is attractive to nearly every one. Even in winter the straight trunks shoot up from the middle of the tree with an orderly arrangement of the branches and twigs, and the huge, conical buds, with their glistening brown hues, are sure to challenge attention. In early spring when—

> " The gray hoss-chestnut's leetle hands unfold,
> Softern a baby's be at three days old,"

the trees have a bizarré effect that cannot be neglected. A little later, when the gray, compound leaves have fully developed and the glorious erect panicles of white blossoms come to their perfection, the Horse-Chestnut is, as the artist Hamerton has said, "a sight for gods and men."

These wonderful blossoms, however, seem primarily intended by nature to attract the visits of the queen bumble-bees, which are abroad during the weeks when the Chestnuts bloom. The expanded, recurved stamens, with projecting style and stigma in their midst, serve as a landing-place for the bees, which are guided to the nectar by the spots of color at the base of the petals. This nectar is protected from the visits of ants and other wingless insects which would steal it without carrying the pollen from blossom to blossom, as do the bumble-bees, by the presence of numerous hairs upon various parts of the flower.

The leaf of this tree is an excellent illustration of a palmately compound leaf. There are usually from five to seven leaflets arranged on the end of the stout petiole, which is much enlarged at its base and which, when it falls off in autumn, reveals a most characteristic leaf-scar which has been frequently likened to a horse-shoe, a series of so-called bundle-scars around the margin serving to represent the nails. Mrs. Dyson writes that in England the tree is sometimes called the Hyacinth Tree and also the Giant's Nosegay, a suggestive name when the tree is in blossom.

HORSE-CHESTNUT

ÆSCULUS HIPPOCASTANUM

COMMON BUCKTHORN

RHAMNUS CATHARTICA

THE COMMON BUCKTHORN

ALTHOUGH there are several native species of Buckthorn belonging to the genus Rhamnus, the one most likely to be known to the resident of the Eastern States is the common European form which has been very generally planted for hedges, and has so frequently developed as an escape from cultivation that it is fairly well naturalized in many localities. In Europe it has such other common names as Hart's-thorn, Waythorn and Rhineberry, but these seem not to be yet used to any extent in America. The important characteristics of the species may be seen in the plate: the leaves are finely serrate on the margins and quite variable in form, though the normal type seems to be oval or ovate; the flowers are borne in short-stemmed clusters the pollen-bearing and the seed-bearing generally being on separate plants, the parts of each blossom being arranged in groups of four; the blackish fruit contains three or four seeds, and the winter-buds are acutely pointed and arranged in opposite pairs. When growing singly the plant takes on the appearance of a shrub-like tree, which may reach a height of twelve to fifteen feet. The species is very useful as a hedge-plant.

In the Southern States the Carolina Buckthorn or Indian Cherry is frequently found, especially in limestone regions. As a tree it may reach a height of forty feet and a trunk diameter of eight inches, though commonly it is of much smaller size. The sweet, round fruit is about one-third of an inch in diameter; it is bright red as it ripens but finally changes to black.

The Bearberry or Coffee-tree is a variable Western species having several distinct varieties which have sometimes been treated of as separate species. "The bark," writes Professor Sargent, "possesses the drastic properties peculiar to that of other species of the genus, and is a popular domestic remedy in Oregon and California, and under the name of Cascara Sagrada has been admitted into the American Materia Medica." The plant has been utilized in landscape planting, though much less generally than the European forms. In addition to the Common Buckthorn, a species from Europe called *Rhamnus Frangula* has been quite generally planted for ornament: it has attractive foliage and fruit, and in some regions is to be found naturalized in fields and woods, the plants probably having come up from seed scattered by birds.

THE LINDEN OR BASSWOOD

THROUGHOUT a large part of its wide range, which extends from New Brunswick south to Georgia, and west to Nebraska and Texas, the American Linden is most generally called the Basswood. It is a well-known tree, growing in a variety of situations and having such definite characteristics that it is easily distinguished by everyone. In earliest spring when drops of dew or rain stand upon the red buds, one is reminded of Tennyson's fine phrase concerning the European Linden:

"A million emeralds break from the ruby-budded lime."

A little later the young leaves push out from these buds in a most interesting manner, and as they develop one can see in the thin blades wonderful adjustments to light, each leaf so placing itself that it will get the largest possible amount of sunshine. The two sides of the obliquely heart-shaped leaf differ greatly in size, that nearest the branch being almost always the larger. Early in summer the curious clusters of blossom-buds appear. They start from the branch as broad yellowish bracts, from near the middle of which the main flower-stalks arise. The flowers are of a greenish-yellow color and secrete nectar in great abundance, to gather which the bees swarm upon them to such an extent that Basswood honey is a recognized product in most apiaries. The poet Bryant wrote:

" The linden in the fervors of July
Hums with a louder concert."

As the summer passes these blossoms gradually develop into curious nut-like fruits which are often called by children "monkey-nuts." These remain upon the tree to a considerable extent after the leaves have fallen, each nut being greenish brown in color with a woody outer covering and generally one seed in a cell inside. Presumably the large bracts help in their dispersal by the wind.

The bark of the Linden-tree is grayish in color, characteristically smooth in young trees and more or less vertically striate in older trees. The wood is so soft that it has long been used for various purposes in cabinet work and in the manufacture of many kinds of woodenware. It is like the European Linden in this respect, of which someone has written:

" Smooth linden best obeys
The carver's chisel ; best his curious works
Displays in nicest touches."

Our American Linden is a very useful tree for ornamental planting and is largely utilized for that purpose. There are certain horticultural varieties sometimes planted, these varieties being mostly forms of the European Linden. Our native species, however, is better adapted to our region, as it is less subject to attack by borers and other insect enemies.

MANGROVE

RHIZOPHORA MANGLE

THE MANGROVE

THE conquest of the sea over the land may be observed all along our northern shores, but the conquest of the land over the sea is best seen along the southern coast, where the Mangrove is the chief agent in the forward movement. In Florida, Louisiana, and Texas, as well as in the Bermudas, Bahamas, and West Indies, one may see this strange tree holding the land already won and ceaselessly reaching out for new acquisitions. The low shrub-like growth seems level and monotonous and is such a tangle of foliage, branches, trunks and descending roots that one needs to analyze the scene with careful scrutiny before each part stands out and reveals the method of the conquest. Making such an analysis, one is likely first to see the curious descending roots coming from the horizontal branches: these are of varying lengths—some just starting, some reaching half way to the water or ground below, and some having their tips firmly imbedded below the surface. These descending roots resemble those of the famous Banyan-tree and form a chief method by which the Mangrove is able to march seaward. They give to the thicket a multitude of trunks which bind the plants firmly together, making an indissoluble colony that can withstand attack by wind and waves. Among the roots and branches the flotsam and jetsam from the sea, and the wind- and water-carried débris from the land finds secure lodgement, and in this material the multitudinous forms of shore-life seek shelter and help to build up a permanent barrier of soil.

One of the most interesting things about the Mangrove is its curious fruit, two of which are shown on the upper part of the plate still attached to the twig. These fruits germinate on the tree, the sickle-like projections in the picture being the caulicles thus sent out. These grow to a length of a foot or less, when they break off and drop to the water below. When they come to rest on shore they send out roots from the lower end and push up leaves from the upper end and thus start a new tree.

Farther inland single Mangroves sometimes assume such a tree-form as is shown on the plate. In such situations the descending branches are likely to be less marked, the tree responding to the conditions of its environment in the way so wonderfully shown in many forms of plant life.

BLUE GUM OR EUCALYPTUS

MORE than fifty species of Eucalyptus are treated of in the "Cyclopedia of Horticulture," and nearly a hundred others are known. Nearly all of these are
native to the Australasian region, although less than half a dozen species are
found in the East Indies. Of this great group the Blue Gum or *Eucalyptus globulus* is
the best known to Europeans and Americans. It is hardy in a climate like that of Central
and Southern California, where the temperature never goes below 25° Fahrenheit, and
grows very rapidly, more so than almost any other tree available for forestry uses. A
diameter of five feet and a height of one hundred and fifty feet is said to be attained in
thirty years. Of its economic uses a leaflet of the Forest Service says: "The wood is
very heavy, hard, strong and tough, but not durable. It is easy to split when first felled,
but not after it is dried. It resembles hickory in many of its qualities but is extremely
difficult to season. The trees are sometimes sawed into lumber and used for wagon work
or agricultural implements, though for none of these purposes is the wood as good as that
of several native species. It is coming into use for piles in sea water, and it appears to
be quite valuable for that purpose although the trials are not yet conclusive. Its chief
value at present is as firewood, for which it is in constant demand in parts of California
where other good fuel is scarce. This recommends it for commercial plantations. Another
important use of the tree is for windbreaks to protect orange and lemon orchards from
the high winds that are prevalent in many parts of the fruit-growing section. No other
tree will make so good a shelter-belt in so short a time." The trees have also been utilized
as windbreaks along harbor shores.

The characteristics of the leaves and fruit are shown in the accompanying plate.
The long, willow-like effect of the former and the curious, box-like structure of the latter
are easily noted. The white flowers have a decided odor, which is unpleasant to mankind
but attractive to insects.

The Red Gum (*E. rostrata*) is a somewhat slower-growing tree than the Blue Gum,
but it has to offset this the advantage of being hardier and of furnishing more durable
lumber. The Sugar Gum (*E. corynocalyx*) can endure drought better than the Red or
Blue species, and furnishes valuable firewood.

BLUE GUM — EUCALYPTUS
EUCALYPTUS GLOBULUS

HERCULES' CLUB — SPINED ARALIA

ARALIA SPINOSA

THE HERCULES' CLUB OR SPINED ARALIA

ONE who is familiar with the appearance of the common herbaceous Spikenard of our woodland borders will easily trace a family resemblance between this plant and the leaves and flowers shown on the plate herewith. Probably the resemblance is more marked in the pictures than it would be in the specimens, because the leaves and flower-clusters of the Hercules' Club are so large that one is likely to think chiefly of their extraordinary size. The familiar Spikenard is known technically as *Aralia racemosa*— the Racemed Aralia—while the Hercules' Club is similarly known as *Aralia spinosa*— the Spined Aralia, a term whose significance is well shown in the picture at the right of the plate. These spines are really formidable and are especially numerous around the nodes that give rise to the great doubly compound leaves. The small picture on the upper left corner of the plate gives a good idea of the general outline of these leaves, but it fails to suggest their enormous size. The distance from the base of the central stalk to the terminal leaflet is often four feet, while the breadth from tip to tip of the side branches is more than half as great. These gigantic leaves appear in the spring as a hairy, bronze green growth that rapidly takes on the shape of the fully-expanded leaves, which finally become dark green on the upper surfaces and light green on the lower surfaces of the leaflets. At the approach of winter they change to a bronzy red color which is commonly more or less suffused with yellow before the leaves drop off.

The Hercules' Club is indigenous to the Southern States, occurring as far north as Pennsylvania, Indiana, and Missouri, and as far west as Eastern Texas. In this region it often occurs in tree-like form with a height of nearly forty feet and a trunk diameter of eight inches, but in more northern regions it is not hardy, winter killing nearly every year, and is likely to take on the appearance of a number of spiny clubs growing close together as shown on the lower left corner of the plate. The tree is decidedly aromatic, a fact which may have led to the use of the small, round, black berries and the bark of the larger roots for medicinal purposes. The fruit ripens late in summer a few weeks after the flowers have made their belated appearance.

One who wishes to get the decorative effect of this species in the Northern States can obtain from the nurseries a closely related hardy tree, originally from Manchuria and China—the Chinese Angelica tree, known technically as *Aralia Chinensis*. At least three varieties of this species are now available: of these the variety *elata*, having few spines upon the bark, is the hardiest and most desirable.

THE TUPELO OR SOUR-GUM TREE

THE Tupelo is a favorite tree with artists on account of the direction of the branches, which seem to radiate from a common centre. In its winter condition it has a most striking individuality, which enables even the novice to recognize it at a glance. It is equally attractive in summer on account of the brilliant green of its dense horizontal foliage, while in autumn it is one of the most brilliantly colored of all our native trees, each leaf taking on a bright scarlet hue which serves to make the mass of foliage one of the most notable elements in the landscape picture. It is essentially a lowland tree, being found in its greatest perfection along the borders of swamps where it is sheltered on one side by the background of the woods. It is widely distributed throughout eastern North America and the names by which it is known vary in an interesting way in different regions. In the Southern States it is universally called the Sour-gum tree; in the western part of its range it is the Pepperidge tree, and in New England it is the Tupelo, the name by which the Indians called it.

The Tupelo is a rather difficult tree to get established, but when once established in a suitable location near a small body of water it is one of the most effective and desirable species. It is easily grown from the seeds contained within the small blue-black drupes, which are generally borne in limited clusters on the ends of rather long fruit-stalks.

In its best estate the Tupelo becomes one hundred feet high with a trunk diameter of five feet, but these mammoth trees occur only rarely and are most likely to be found on the slopes of the southern Appalachian Mountains. Throughout most of its range the tree is barely half this size. The wood of the larger trees is often converted into lumber which is used for various manufacturing purposes, especially for wheel-hubs and ox-yokes.

Two other species of the Tupelo genus occur in the Southern States. The Sour Tupelo or Ogeechee Lime (*Nyssa Ogeche*) is a swamp loving species found in the Ogeechee Valley and adjacent localities. The small trees bear sour, juicy, red fruits, which render them conspicuous. The Aquatic Tupelo or Cotton Gum (*Nyssa aquatica*) is a much larger tree found in Cypress swamps. It reaches a height of one hundred feet and a trunk diameter of four feet. The purple fruits hang on long stems.

TUPELO — PEPPERIDGE — SOUR GUM

NYSSA SYLVATICA

FLOWERING DOGWOOD

CORNUS FLORIDA

DOGWOOD FAMILY

THE FLOWERING DOGWOOD

THROUGHOUT a large part of the central and southern regions of the United States the Flowering Dogwood, at least when in blossom, is known to everyone. It is found from Massachusetts west to Ontario and Michigan, and south to Florida, Missouri, and Texas, and it occurs commonly in rich woodlands, generally under the shelter of taller, deciduous trees. In the more northern parts of its range it is rather a rare tree, but in the South it is abundant. It seldom reaches a height greater than forty feet or a trunk diameter larger than eighteen inches, and in the north it is more likely to be a shrub than a tree. Whatever its size and form, when the Dogwood is in blossom before or with the unfolding leaves, it is certain to attract the attention of every observer. On the ends of the upturned twigs there appear to be enormous flowers of a pinkish white or greenish color. These are really clusters of flowers, each cluster of rather inconspicuous greenish blossoms being surrounded by four large bracts which give to the group its conspicuous appearance. They also serve to attract a variety of insects to help in carrying the pollen from blossom to blossom and from tree to tree. After the flowers have been pollenized the bracts drop off and the fruit gradually develops, attaining full size late in summer and commonly remaining on until autumn as somewhat egg-shaped, red or scarlet drupes, averaging half an inch in length.

After the leaves have fallen in autumn the twigs are rather easily distinguished, the bark being distinctly downy and grayish in color. When both leaf-buds and flower-buds are present, the former may be known by their small size and conical shape, and the latter by their larger size and very rounded shape with projecting tips. The wood of this tree is of great value on account of its hardness, being used for the handles of many tools. It weighs fifty pounds per cubic foot and is brown in color with a fine, firm texture that has led it often to be called Boxwood. The bitter bark was formerly believed to have a tonic value as a medicine, and the Indians used to obtain from the bark of the roots a scarlet dye.

The Flowering Dogwood is of extraordinary value in landscape planting, especially for shady situations and for shrubby effects. It is hardy throughout its range, but farther north it is likely to be winter killed. It is comparatively free from insect or fungus enemies but grows rather slowly. In addition to the typical form, which is of especial value for its white flowers in early summer and its red foliage in autumn, the nurserymen offer a red-flowering variety and a weeping variety. In the northern limits of its range the tree is rather uncertain in its flowering, the bracts sometimes being greenish and abortive.

THE ALTERNATE-LEAVED DOGWOOD

THE adjective phrase used in naming this species indicates one of its chief characteristics. While the other Dogwoods have opposite leaves, in this form they are generally alternate. This alternation is somewhat irregular, however, there being a tendency to grouping in more or less definite whorls, especially next the flower-clusters, in a way well shown in the accompanying plate. The leaves themselves have the peculiar texture with sunken veins and smooth margins characteristic of many of the Dogwoods. In its best estate this species becomes a small tree twenty-five feet high, but more commonly it is smaller and more or less shrub-like, with flat spreading branches arising in irregular whorls upon the main stem. The attractive clusters of yellowish flowers appear late in spring or early in summer, and are followed in autumn by the good-sized bluish black berries borne at the ends of branching stems of an attractive red color. The berries are eaten by so many kinds of birds that they are likely to gone before winter. The twigs in winter are greenish, sometimes purplish, and the species is frequently called the Green Osier Dogwood.

This Alternate-leaved Dogwood is one of the most characteristic features of the underwoods in Northern forests. It is widely distributed, occurring from Nova Scotia south to Alabama, and west to Minnesota. It is especially attractive in autumn when the foliage takes on a deep purplish red color, and the fruits and fruit-stems are also colored in contrasting hues. The species is of decided value in ornamental planting, the chief objection to it for this purpose being that it is subject to a disease, probably of bacterial origin, somewhat similar to pear-blight. The young trees are commonly offered by nurserymen, or may be transplanted from the woods. Two horticultural varieties have already been introduced: in one the whorled effect of the horizontal branches is more marked than in the wild plant; in the other, the leaves are marked with white.

There are several other Dogwoods in our native flora. The Rough-leaved Dogwood (*Cornus asperifolia*) is widely distributed through the West, a shrub in the North and a tree in the South. You may know it by its white berries and its leaves roughened by stiff hairs. The Pacific Dogwood was named by one ornithologist in honor of another: *Cornus Nutallii* Audubon will immediately awaken interest in the mind of any one interested in birds and bird books. The large six-bracted blossoms are suggestive of those of the Flowering Dogwood of the east, and it lights up the western forests in much the same way that the latter lights up the eastern woods.

ALTERNATE-LEAVED DOGWOOD

CORNUS ALTERNIFOLIA

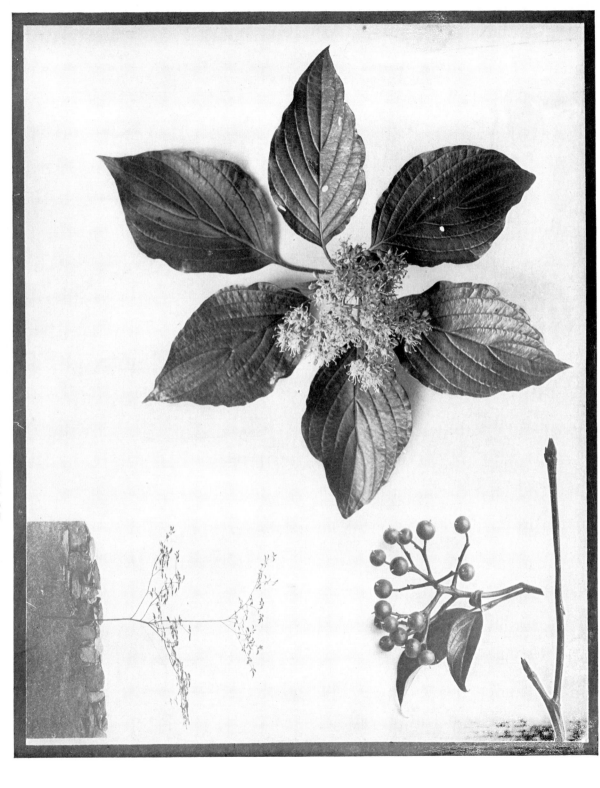

RHODODENDRON — GREAT LAUREL — ROSE BAY

RHODODENDRON MAXIMUM

THE GREAT LAUREL OR ROSE BAY

THE extraordinary beauty of our native Rhododendron or Rose Bay is universally acknowledged. Its only rival is the Mountain Laurel of the same heath family and having very similar characteristics. No other native plant could possibly be confused with it: the long, thick, smooth-margined, evergreen leaves, clustered at the ends of the branches; the beautiful white or rosy pink flowers, with petals of such delicate texture; the dark, brownish-red fruit-capsules, with the dried pistils projecting from their tips; and the large flower-buds—these are all distinctive features of the species so far as native plants are concerned. In parks and private grounds Rhododendrons of other species have been planted in great variety, so that the determination of the precise sort in such a planting is a much more difficult matter.

As commonly found in the woods our Rhododendron is a shrub, commonly more or less spreading in its habit of growth, but in its largest estate it may become a tree forty feet high and a foot in diameter, although even then it is likely to give the effect of an overgrown bush, its trunk being very short and generally crooked and irregular in outline. The species occurs locally from Nova Scotia southward, but only in great numbers in Southern mountain regions.

A great many hybrid forms of Rhododendron have been developed by crossing this and other species. Many of these are hardy and of great beauty and are extensively planted by landscape architects. The demand, however, so exceeds the supply of well-grown plants that during recent years great quantities of the native forms have been transplanted from the woods. On this subject Mr. J. Woodward Manning writes in the "Cyclopedia of Horticulture:" "Such large private estates as those of William Rockefeller W. L. Elkins, Mrs. Eliot F. Shepard and others have very largely been stocked with collected plants of *Rhododendron maximum*, supplied in car-load lots and in sizes ranging from 8-foot bushy specimens down to small plants that could be grown for future flower and foliage effects. These plants are taken from localities where the plants are growing either in the open or under moderate shade conditions, and have been pruned by the natural process of fire, resulting in a vigorous growth of a more or less bushy and compact nature and growing in a soil of sufficient richness to assure their digging with a large amount of clinging earth. With proper care in transportation and after-cultivation the results show a surprisingly small loss of plants." Of course this method can only be temporary, for the plants growing under the most favorable conditions for digging are limited, but it will enable the nurseries to develop a supply for future use.

THE MOUNTAIN LAUREL

WITH the possible exception of the Rhododendron, no American shrub is more beautiful when in blossom than the Mountain Laurel, which is widely distributed over the eastern region of North America, ranging from New Brunswick to Florida, and extending westward to Ohio and Tennessee. It is a favorite with every lover of the woods who has seen it in blossom, or has even come across the shining green decorative leaves at any season. It is by no means generally distributed over the region indicated, being found especially in hilly localities, but often being only local, even there. Many people who have never seen it growing wild, know it because of its popularity for ornamental planting and for holiday decorations.

It blossoms in May or June, according to the locality and elevation and bears the good-sized flowers in wonderful clusters, sure to attract attention. These clusters, grouped at the ends of the branches, consist of a considerable number of large flowers, the single blossoms being rendered extremely attractive by the broadly salver-shaped united petals. The pollen-bearing anthers are caught in curious little pockets in these petals and so held on their supports that when an insect visits the flower to gather nectar the anthers are released and shower the pollen upon the visitor.

Its use for decorative purposes threatens the extermination of this beautiful shrub in many localities. It is robbed of the flowers for church and home decoration, as well as for sale on the city streets, and vast quantities of its branches are gathered and sold during the Christmas holidays. In some regions the species is called Calico Bush, perhaps from the spotted buds and blossoms, and in others it used to be called Spoonwood because the Indians made cooking utensils from it.

A more generally distributed though less attractive species of Laurel is the Sheep Laurel or Lamb-kill, a low-growing shrub found from the Hudson Bay region south to Georgia. It seldom reaches a greater height than three feet, and bears rather small flowers. which seem miniature reproductions of the blossoms of the Mountain Laurel, but of a deeper red color.

This Lamb-kill derives its common name from the fact that the foliage is poisonous, and when eaten by sheep and lambs often causes death. It is consequently dreaded in sheep pastures, and, in fact, has no such claims for preservation as has the Mountain Laurel, which also occasionally leads to the death of stock, so that in regions where domestic animals graze it may be desirable to reduce or exterminate the Laurel. It is not in such regions, however, that it is likely to be gathered for decorative purposes.

Both these plants belong to the genus Kalmia, the name being given in honor of Peter Kalm, who traveled in North America during the middle of the Eighteenth century, The Mountain Laurel is known technically as *Kalmia latifolia*, while the Sheep Laurel is *K. angustifolia*. There are various varieties of each species.

MOUNTAIN LAUREL
KALMIA LATIFOLIA

SOURWOOD — SORREL-TREE
OXYDENDRUM ARBOREUM

THE SOURWOOD OR SORREL-TREE

ONE who is familiar with the beautiful bell-shaped or urn-shaped flowers of the Cassandra or Andromeda shrubs common in the Northern States will readily recognize in the cluster of flowers pictured on the plate the distinctive character-istics of the Andromeda group of the heath family. These flowers, which appear in June or July against the shining bronze green background of the leaves, render the Sourwood a very attractive tree, and its beauty is almost equally striking when in autumn the leaves take on a vivid scarlet color. These features, together with its hardiness in the North, render it a very desirable tree for ornamental planting: even the fact that it grows slowly may be an advantage to one who wishes to use it in borders among other shrubs.

As a native tree the Sourwood is said by Sargent to occur on "well-drained, gravelly soil on ridges rising above the banks of streams; Southeastern Pennsylvania to Southern Indiana and Middle Tennessee, and southward to the coast of Virginia and along the Alleghany Mountains to Western Florida, the shores of Mobile Bay and through the elevated regions of the Gulf states to Western Louisiana; of its largest size on the slopes of the Big Smoky Mountains, Tennessee." In the latter situation it becomes a tree sixty feet high with a trunk diameter of twenty inches. In trees of good size the bark of the trunk is deeply furrowed. The buds are partially sunken in the bark of the twigs, and there is no terminal bud. The leaves have a distinctly acid taste, to which is due the two com-mon names and the technical genus name—*Oxydendrum*—of the species.

A large proportion of the members of the heath family are shrubs, but there are a few other tree-forms found in North America in addition to the Mountain Laurel, Rhododendron, and Sourwood. These are mostly rare and local species, little known except to the professional botanist. One of these, named Elliottia, in honor of a noted Southern botanist, is found locally in Georgia. Then there are three species of the beautiful Madroñas, belonging to the genus *Arbutus*, which occur in the far Western States, and a single tree-like form of the Cranberry group—the Sparkleberry belonging to the genus *Vaccinium*—which is rather widely distributed in the Southern States.

THE PERSIMMON

FOR some reason, which I find rather difficult to explain, the Persimmon and the opossum are always associated in my consciousness. Probably it is because the two species occupy somewhat similar positions in the dialect literature of the South, the Persimmon fruits being as famous among trees in the folk-lore tales of the South as is the opossum among animals. At any rate, they are both extraordinary forms, being the sole representatives of their families in eastern America and occupying a very similar geographical range. Even their scientific names are not unlike, the Persimmon being known technically as *Diospyros Virginiana*, while the opossum is *Didelphis Virginiana*.

The Persimmon is essentially a Southern tree, being most abundant in the States along the South Atlantic and the Gulf coasts, extending as far north as Southern Ohio. It has been reported as being found in southern New England but there seems to be reason for believing that some of these trees at least were not indigenous. The fruit is the most interesting feature of the tree, being of good size and a favorite article of food after its astringency has been removed by the action of frost. The form and character of the fruits are shown upon the plate. These develop from flowers that blossom in June, there being pollen-bearing and seed-bearing flowers upon different branches of the same tree or upon different trees. These blossoms are a pale yellow color and of the general forms illustrated on the plate, the smaller pollen-bearing ones being shown above the larger seed-bearing ones.

One of the earliest references to the Persimmon has been quoted by Miss Keeler in her excellent book upon "Our Native Trees:" it is found in "The Historie of Travaile into Virginia Brittania," and reads as follows:

"They have a plumb which they call pessemmins, like to a medler, in England, but of a deeper tawnie cullour; they grow on a most high tree. When they are not fully ripe, they are harsh and choakie, and furre in a man's mouth like allam, howbeit, being taken fully ripe, yt is a reasonable pleasant fruict, somewhat lushious. I have seen our people put them into their baked and sodden puddings; there be those whose tast allows them to be as pretious as the English apricock; I confess it is a good kind of horse plumb."

There is great variation in the size and quality of fruits from different trees, and it would seem feasible greatly to improve the edible characters of the fruit from trees planted by men, by a little attention to the selection of seed or by budding or grafting.

PERSIMMON

BLUE ASH

THE BLUE ASH

THE Blue Ash is perhaps the easiest to identify of all the Ashes. At any season it may be known by the four-angled character of the twigs, there being four distinct ridges running lengthwise along the bark. It also has other specific characteristics. In autumn and winter it shows the short, broad keys which are slightly suggestive of those of the Black Ash; in spring it shows flowers which have both stamens and pistils in the same blossoms, instead of in separate blossoms on separate trees as in the other Ashes; in summer its inner bark reveals a blue coloring when mixed with water. The use of this coloring as a dye led to the name Blue Ash.

This species seems to be especially a native of the Mississippi Valley, occurring from Southern Michigan to Iowa on the north, and from Tennessee to Arkansas on the south. It commonly grows on uplands, though occasionally found on lowlands, and generally occurs as a tall tree, perhaps seventy feet high, though occasionally decidedly higher. It is an excellent tree for street and park planting.

In his "Manual of the Trees of North America" Professor Sargent enumerates sixteen species of native Ash trees. The ten additional to the six important sorts treated of herewith are comparatively unimportant trees, with limited geographical ranges. Two species, which have the common name of Water Ash, are found in swamps in the Southern States and are closely akin to our Black Ash. One, called the Mountain Ash, is found in Texas. Another, called the Pumpkin Ash, is a splendid tree growing in swamps in Missouri, Arkansas, and Florida, and having a buttressed base probably because its roots are so constantly under water. The paddle-like keys are unusually large, commonly reaching a length of three inches. The Biltmore Ash is an interesting Southern form, seldom attaining a large size.

A number of sorts of Ash trees from Europe are found in cultivation. Most of these are the typical form or a variety of the European Ash (*Fraxinus excelsior*). Like so many trees that have been long in cultivation it has many horticultural varieties, ten of which are enumerated by Alfred Rehder in the "Cyclopedia of Horticulture." One of these has the leaflets margined with white; another blotched with white; another has yellow branches; another has very slender leaflets; another has the leaflets curled and twisted; still another has simple rather than compound leaflets, while some varieties have pendent branches. These special varieties are reproduced by budding just as varieties of fruit trees are reproduced.

THE BLACK ASH

IN summer and autumn the Black Ash is readily distinguished by the sessile leaflets and the very broad key-fruits, the latter having the part which holds the seed much flattened and surrounded by a wing-like projection. In winter the young twigs are not pubescent and the buds are very black. In spring the tree comes into blossom early in May as the leaves are developing, the seed-bearing and the pollen-bearing flowers being borne on different trees.

It is perhaps as a timber tree that the Black Ash is most famous. Even before the settlement of America by the whites this was a favorite tree with the Indians, who preferred it to all other species for the manufacture of baskets. For this purpose the wood is beaten with mallets until it is so softened that it is easily split into long plaits. One of its chief advantages as a timber tree is the fact that it grows to a great height with very little decrease in diameter, and it is also extraordinarily free from knots and other blemishes.

The Black Ash is essentially a tree of swamps and lowlands. It frequently grows along sluggish streams but is not so likely to be found along ordinary river banks as is the White Ash or the Red Ash. It ranges from the Gulf of St. Lawrence westward to Manitoba and southward to Arkansas and Virginia. Like the other Ash trees this species sheds its foliage rather early in autumn and comes into leaf rather late in spring. The latter characteristic they share with the European Ash, of which Tennyson wrote the familiar lines:

"Why lingereth she to clothe her heart with love,
Delaying as the tender Ash delays
To clothe itself, when all the woods are green?"

The Black Ash is also often called the Swamp Ash and Brown Ash, and in some localities the Basket Ash or Hoop Ash. It is not so generally planted as an ornamental tree as is the White Ash, but it may be used to advantage in wet soil where slender, tall trees are desired. In such situations it appears to best advantage in groups rather than singly.

BLACK ASH
FRAXINUS NIGRA

WHITE ASH
FRAXINUS AMERICANA

THE WHITE ASH

FEW trees have a more characteristic appearance at any season of the year than do our various species of the Ash-tree family. The bark of the trunk is of a grayish color, and is so vertically furrowed in a more or less zigzag fashion as to be easily recognized. The manner of growth of the branches and twigs is also characteristic, as are the large compound leaves and the very distinctive paddle-like key-fruits.

The European Ash has been the subject of many traditions and superstitions, which to a certain extent have been applied to the American species. One of the most curious of these is the one relating to the antipathy of snakes for the branches of the trees. So long ago as Pliny wrote, the superstition apparently was in existence, for that author states that the serpent will go through fire rather than through the branches of the Ash tree.

The White Ash is distinguished in summer from the other species native to America by having stalked leaflets on glabrous petioles, the leaflets being distinctly whiter on the under than on the upper surface. The margins of the leaflets are serrate and the tips are commonly acuminate. They turn yellow in autumn. In winter the White Ash is distinguished by having smooth glabrous twigs and slender key-fruits on which the wing is terminal.

The curious blossoms of this tree are sent out in spring in advance of the leaves. The pollen-bearing and the seed-bearing flowers are generally on different trees, and the pollen is evidently carried by the wind. The seed-bearing flowers are in long panicles that become still larger as the fruit matures.

The White Ash grows commonly throughout a vast region bounded by Nova Scotia and Minnesota on the north, and Florida and Texas on the south. It is greatly prized as a timber tree, the wood being used for many purposes, and it also has decided advantages as a shade and ornamental tree. It is often called the American Ash, the translation of its technical name. It is easily grown from seed.

THE RED ASH

THE Red Ash or River Ash is easily recognized at any season of the year by the distinct pubescence upon the bark of the young twigs. In summer the leaflets are seen to be distinctly stalked like those of the White Ash, but differing from that species in that the stalks, the petioles, and more or less of the under surface of the leaves, are covered with fine hairs. The under surface of the blade is lighter green than the upper surface. In autumn the leaflets become first yellowish, then brownish, falling to the ground rather early. The fruit is similar to that of the White Ash, except that the wing instead of being terminal extends well down the sides of the basal seed-bearing parts.

The Red Ash is a rare tree in comparison with the abundant White Ash. It occurs along river banks and is found over a wide territory, extending from New Brunswick to Manitoba on the north, to Dakota and Missouri on the west, and to Alabama and Florida on the south. Like the Black Ash it is sometimes called the Brown Ash. It is easily started from seed, and has almost as many claims for landscape planting as has the White Ash

The Red Ash is one of the trees most easily recognized in winter on account of the grayish pubescence on the bark of the young branches. The surface of the bark is marked by slight longitudinal striations and numerous whitish oval dots which are often concealed by the pubescence. The buds are dark brown, and rather small, with the surface of the scales distinctly downy. The terminal buds are broadly wedge-shaped, while the others are generally rounded.

Three horticultural forms of the Red Ash have already been developed: in one of these the leaflets are blotched with yellow and are not so hairy as in the normal type; in another the leaflets are very dark, shining green; in the third the leaflets are also dark, shining green but are much larger and more slender.

RED ASH

FRAXINUS PENNSYLVANICA

GREEN ASH

FRAXINUS PENNSYLVANICA — VAR LANCEOLATA

THE GREEN ASH

THERE has been considerable discussion in regard to the specific relationship of the Red Ash and the tree which is commonly called the Green Ash, a sort which differs chiefly in having the bark of the twigs smooth. By many botanists the Green Ash is classified as a variety of the Red. The gist of the matter seems to have been concisely stated by Professor C. S. Sargent, who writes: "East of the Mississippi River the Red and Green Ashes grow side by side and retain their individual character; but in the West they are connected by intermediate forms which can be referred to one as well as to the other."

The general characters of the species are well shown on the plate. The slender leaflets have distinctly serrate margins and are shining green both above and below, to which fact its common name is due.

The tree has a round top and the bark of the twigs lacks the hairy covering that is characteristic of the Red Ash. The blossoms appear as the leaves are developing, the pollen-bearing flowers in small clusters on one tree and the seed-bearing flowers in longer panicles on another tree. The paddle-like fruits are indistinguishable from those of the Red Ash.

The Green Ash seems to be most abundant and distinctive in the region between the Alleghany Mountains and the Mississippi River: although abundant west of that river it is more likely to intergrade into the Red Ash. In this region, however, it is one of the most valuable trees for purposes of forestry and shade, and has been very largely planted upon the plains, where it thrives in comparatively dry situations.

On the Pacific Slope there is a splendid Ash tree called the Oregon Ash—*Fraxinus Oregona*—which compares favorably with the best forms in the more eastern regions. The tree reaches a height of eighty feet and a trunk diameter of four feet, and occurs as a forest growth in the valleys of water-courses. The lumber is of much value and is used for a great variety of purposes.

THE EASTERN CATALPA OR INDIAN BEAN

THE Catalpa is one of the few trees which rivals the Horse-Chestnut in glorious beauty during the period of blossoming. The great panicles of showy flowers borne on the ends of the branches against the leafy background of the newly-developed foliage render the tree one of the most conspicuous objects in the landscape, and serve to attract the attention of the most indifferent human observer, as well as the eager presence of swarms of bumble-bees and other insects which cross-pollenize the flowers in return for the nectar and pollen furnished by the latter. These flowers are soon succeeded by the slender, thin-walled pods, which slowly mature through the summer until in autumn, when the leaves fall off, they have reached a length of eight to twelve inches and serve as a ready means of identifying the tree during late autumn and early winter, as they hang from the tips of the smaller twigs.

Two distinct species of native Catalpas are recognized by the best authorities. The Eastern Catalpa, as it is called, is the species represented on the opposite plate. It has slender pods with thin walls and the tips of the leaf are short-pointed; the inside of the flower is thickly spotted with reddish dots and the lower lobe is generally entire. The technical name of this species is *Catalpa Catalpa*. The Western or Hardy Catalpa has stout pods with thick walls, and the tip of the leaf is long-pointed; the inside of the flower is not thickly spotted with colored dots, and the lower lobe of the corolla is generally notched at the tip. The technical name of this species is *Catalpa speciosa*.

The Eastern Catalpa is believed to have occurred originally in certain of the South-eastern States, especially Georgia, Alabama, and Florida, from whence it has been generally distributed through the South. In the East it is hardy as far north as Massachusetts, and has been largely planted for ornamental purposes. At least three well-marked horticultural varieties have been developed from it: one of these has yellow leaves; another has purplish leaves, especially in spring; and the third assumes a round, compact, bush-like form.

WESTERN OR HARDY CATALPA
CATALPA SPECIOSA

BIGNONIACEÆ

BIGNONIA FAMILY

THE WESTERN OR HARDY CATALPA

FOUR of the most important specific characters of this species are shown in the plate; the pods are stouter and have thicker walls than those of the Eastern Catalpa; the flowers, which appear about two weeks earlier than those of the eastern form, are in smaller clusters and the inside of the corolla is comparatively free from spots; the leaves have long, slender, acutely-pointed tips. In addition to these distinctions, the bark of the trunk in good-sized trees is furrowed in the Western and scaly in the Eastern Catalpa. In its native forest the tree of the Hardy Catalpa reaches twice the height of the Eastern species.

Originally indigenous to a comparatively limited region in the Mississippi Valley, the Hardy Catalpa has become naturalized through planting by man over a large part of the United States. It is able to endure the climate as far north as 44° and its unusual value for forest planting has long been recognized; the trees are easily raised from seed; they grow rapidly and are comparatively free from enemies, while the wood has an extraordinary ability to resist decay when in contact with water. This latter property renders the timber of especial value for fence-posts, railway-ties, and similar purposes.

In the parks and private grounds of many cities the Japanese Catalpa has been very generally planted. This may readily be known from our native trees: the flowers which appear in June are yellow rather than white, and are spotted and striped on their inner surfaces with violet and orange; the leaves are often lobed; the fruit-pods are very long and slender. The trees do not attain a large size, but they are very attractive and are more hardy than our Eastern Catalpa. There is also available for ornamental planting at least one excellent hybrid between the Japanese and the Eastern Catalpa: it is known as Teas' Japan Hybrid. It has whitish flowers in very large and beautiful clusters.

It is very desirable that more of these various ornamental Catalpas be planted; they add beauty and variety to our cities and villages, and are so easy to grow and so free from attack by enemies that they will thrive even with the neglect that our trees are so likely to get after they are once set out.

THE SHEEPBERRY OR SWEET VIBURNUM

OF all the trees and shrubs to be found in our fields and woods none is easier to distinguish in winter than the Sheepberry, Nannyberry, or Sweet Viburnum The long, slender, reddish-brown, scurfy buds are unique; the terminal ones that are to develop blossoms are swollen at the base in the characteristic manner shown in the twig pictured on the plate. At other seasons the species can also be readily known; in summer the leaf-stems have winged margins and the tips of the blades are somewhat acuminate; the small whitish flowers which blossom in spring or early summer are clustered in fragrant flattened cymes, and are succeeded by the characteristic bluish-black, oblong, more or less flattened fruits, generally having a glaucous bloom over the surface, which are about one-half inch long and ripen early in autumn. These fruits are freely eaten by a considerable variety of birds. The species is widely distributed in eastern North America, occurring as far west as Wyoming and Nebraska. In its best estate it is an attractive tree about twenty-five feet high, but more commonly it is a shrub growing along stone walls and the borders of the forest.

"There is a softness and richness about the flowers and foliage of the Sweet Viburnum," wrote George B. Emerson in his classic report on the Trees and Shrubs of Massachusetts, "which distinguish it above all others of the same genus. It is hardly less beautiful in fruit, from the profusion of the rich blue berries hanging down among the curled leaves, which are beginning to assume the beautiful hues of autumn. A tree of this kind makes a fine appearance at the angle of a walk, or in the corner of a garden, as its delicacy invites a near approach, and rewards examination. With this delicacy of appearance it is a hardy plant, and may sometimes be seen on a bleak hillside, where it has encountered the northwest winds for a score of years."

More than thirty distinct species of Viburnum are discussed in the "Cyclopedia of Horticulture:" more than one-third of these are native to North America. In addition to the Nannyberry the most important tree-forms are the Rusty Nannyberry (*V. rufidulum*), a Southern species, and the Black Haw or Stag Bush (*V. prunifolium*). There are a number of interesting shrubs belonging to the genus Viburnum: of these the Hobble-bush or American Wayfaring Tree is one of the most important. It is very generally distributed as a part of the underwoods in Northern forests, and is especially notable for its beautiful flower-clusters in early summer and its glorious, dark-red foliage in autumn. The Arrowwood (*V. dentatum*) is a widely distributed shrub which derives its name from the use of the branches for arrows by the Indians. The Cranberry Bush or High Bush Cranberry is *Viburnum Opulus* and is widely distributed: the Snowball, which was formerly so popular, is a variety of this species.

SWEET VIBURNUM — SHEEPBERRY
VIBURNUM LENTAGO

INDEX

INDEX

INDEX

INDEX

INDEX

INDEX

INDEX